'Num
be written on tl
the doorway to the world of intellectual
adventure...

My purpose of narrating this wonderful
story is to take away any fear a child may
have of numbers. Numbers are fun,
numbers are magical. It is my hope that
this story will inspire parents and
teachers to enthuse children with a
life-long love for numbers and maths.'

Shakuntala Devi

With missionary zeal Shakuntala Devi has been pursuing her lifetime objective of demystifying numbers and making them a part of every person's daily creative energy. She believes numbers are fun; she believes anyone can enjoy numbers, specially children. To give shape to her dreams of making maths a fun activity for younger children, now she is working on setting up a maths institute in Karnataka, India.

Hailing from a Brahmin family, Shakuntala Devi was initiated to maths by her grandfather and by the age of five hailed as a prodigy. She wants people to shed their phobia of maths, which tends to get communicated to children. Through her eminently readable books and highly entertaining lectures she has done much to help people get friendly with numbers. It is when maths is approached in a spirit of fun, she says, only then can we put it to its most complete use and extract the greatest mileage from it in terms of application.

IN THE
WONDERLAND
OF
NUMBERS
········Maths and Your Child········

Shakuntala Devi

Orient Paperbacks

DELHI | MUMBAI | HYDERABAD

ISBN : 978-81-222-0399-8

In the Wonderland of Numbers: Maths and Your Child

Subject: Education / Parenting

© Shakuntala Devi

1st Published 2006
7th Printing 2013

Published by
Orient Paperbacks
(A division of Vision Books Pvt. Ltd.)
5A/8 Ansari Road, New Delhi-110 002
www.orientpaperbacks.com

Cover design & Inside Illustrations by Ani Das

Printed at
Anand Sons, Delhi-110 092, India

Cover Printed at
Ravindra Printing Press, Delhi-110 006, India

Contents

Contents

'As for numbers, they hate
nobody and nobody can afford
to hate them.'

— Shakuntala Devi

1

Of Friends and Foes

The crisp morning air contained none of the heat which dominated the rest of the day. Birds chirped and the sweet sound of devotional music, being played in many homes in the neighbourhood, reached Neha's ears as she bent over the damp patch in front of her doorstep. She loved to draw the decorative patterns called *kolam* or *rangoli* and usually came to do this pleasant task soon after brushing her teeth.

As she bent over the pattern, the rattle of a moped sounded around the corner and Seenu the milkman came into view.

'Good morning, Neha!' said the milkman cheerily. He was extremely fond of this particular nine-year-old customer. He took out four milk sachets from the huge canvas bags slung on the sides of his two-wheeler and handed them to the little girl. 'What a beautiful *kolam*!' he exclaimed admiringly.

'Thank you, Seenu *Mama*,' said Neha, smiling. She was used to her milkman friend's consistent admiration. Both he and his wife stayed to exchange a few words with Neha whenever they saw her. Her bright face and sprightly gait comforted them, making them less mindful of not having any children of their own.

In fact, both Seenu and Neha would have stood and chatted longer had an irate voice not hailed them from a nearby house. 'Hey Seenu!' it said. 'Are you going to make us wait forever for our morning coffee?'

Neha grinned guiltily and gathered up the pot of *kolam* powder. Seenu walked away to his milk-laden moped, but not before he had turned and waved once more at Neha. She waved and went indoors to get ready for school. However early she began, it was always a difficult task to get to the school bus stop on time. As it is, her mother was already shouting 'Neha-a-a!' from the depths of the house.

'Coming, *Amma*!' she called back. The day had well and truly begun.

Some days got over as well as they had started. Neha returned home from school that afternoon still cheerful.

'Look Neha! Your friend is waiting for you as usual!' said Neha's friend Jyoti with some excitement, as she peered from the window of the school van. Neha glanced out too. She smiled at the sight of a large elephant standing near a temple on the side of the road. She picked up her bag and prepared to get off, waving goodbye to Jyoti.

She got off the school bus at the temple every afternoon. From there her home was a short walk away. Neha Ramachandran usually stopped at the temple every day before she walked home. The temple elephant, a large, beautiful seven-year old named Shakti, was stationed outside the broad wooden gates of the shrine. As soon as Shakti saw Neha each day, she would begin to move her head up and down, as if she was greeting her nine-year old friend.

11

Neha responded by running up to the elephant and holding out a little banana that she had been saving up all day just for this. The banana was packed by her mother every day to provide her some extra vitamins in school, but her mother had no idea that it was a tasty treat Neha saved for Shakti, the temple elephant.

Muthuraman, the elephant's keeper — a short, round, balding man — always had a smile for Neha. 'Here's your special friend, Shakti!' he would address the elephant when he saw Neha. 'How is Neha Devi?' he would continue. Neha would smile at him, but her attention would actually be on the elephant.

Shakti accepted the friendly offering and blessed her.

After these minutes of silent companionship, Neha usually hurried home, hoping to find her mother in a good mood. That day Neha's mother was smiling as she reached home and Neha was glad. This meant that her father had found a job again and might even continue working there for some weeks or even months. She knew her mother's moods were most often connected with her father being out of work. But she still wished there were more smiles than scolds, even though she could not share the difficulties of her father and mother's adult world.

Neha lived in Shyamalapuram, a small town close to Trichy, in Tamil Nadu. Her home was a small house in a row of similar houses, with a street in front of it. This street was noisy in the summer with the sound of playing children, but in the other seasons it usually turned quiet in the evenings, with all the children settling down to their books. Doing well in their studies was considered very, very important for the children in Shyamalapuram. Their parents emphasised that this was the only way the children could grow to have important jobs in the outside world and become world famous doctors, engineers, mathematicians or scientists.

Neha's mother's name was Lakshmi and there were only two reasons why she turned cross and grumpy. One was when Neha's father had just resigned or been turned away from a job. The other was when she came to pick up Neha from school on the odd afternoon, and spent some time listening to the mothers of other children at the school gates.

Neha called these mothers 'trouble-making mammas' but only in her own head. How could she tell her mother about this nickname when her mother took these women so seriously? These ladies would gloat over the wonderful doings of their offspring. Neha's mother would return home rattled about Neha's marks.

Not that she need have worried unduly. Neha was a good student who enjoyed studying and sailed through her tests. That is all tests except her Maths tests, conducted by her Maths teacher Ms. Eswaran. In these she had lately been faring very badly indeed.

It was awful. Before Ms. Eswaran became Neha's teacher, she had always been able to do her sums with speed and add or multiply or subtract or divide with the rest of the class, getting the right answers. After this teacher arrived and began explaining fractions in her high, nasal voice, Neha felt hopelessly confused. When she asked questions about all the doubts that were gathering force in her head, Ms. Eswaran turned very snappy and nasty and poor Neha subsided. She did not want to look ridiculous in front of the class.

So Ms. Eswaran became a figure to dread and the numbers that used to seem understandable to Neha, also became hostile and scary. She stopped doing well in Maths, or putting up her hand eagerly to answer questions in class. Instead, she turned cold with fear when Ms. Eswaran's high pitched voice cut into her classroom thoughts. 'Let us ask Neha now what the product of $3\frac{6}{7}$ and $5\frac{3}{4}$ is,' she would say, with a falsely sweet smile on her face and the whole class would turn to look at a stammering and stuttering Neha. She would be standing in her place and staring at the teacher, unable to think of a single correct suggestion to solve the sum.

Soon the teacher's pointing out to Neha became the signal for the class to have a laugh at her utter discomfort for a few seconds, before they went on with their lesson. Neha's newfound terror of Maths and her inability to get good marks in a subject that she used to be once quite comfortable with became common knowledge. It became a big worry for Neha's mother.

She would pull angrily at Neha's hair, when she sat down to apply oil to Neha's head and comb her hair. Neha had a head full of thick, wiry hair inclined to curl and get into knots. Her mother would pull at these with frustration saying, 'Your hair is like your grandmother's,' referring to Neha's father's mother, who had thick, curly hair even after it had all turned silvery white. Then she would give another tug at a stubborn knot, making Neha swallow an 'Ouch' of pain, and continue, 'Maybe you have inherited her

15

brain as well.' Neha would say nothing. What was there to say? Her grandmother was loving and kind. She was the only one in her family to have stayed content with a school education, when every other person had a college degree. Neha's father always told stories about how playful and wilful she had been as a child — a complete tomboy in the 1940s! Now she lived in Delhi with Neha's uncle.

Her mother was not only smiling when Neha reached home, but greeted her with freshly made ribbon *pakoras* and a sweet *halwa* called *kesari bhaat*. As Neha crunched on the savoury *pakoras*, which curled into brown ribbon shapes, she asked, '*Appa*'s new job is at a garment factory, isn't it *Amma*?'

'Yes dear,' her mother replied. 'It's the new, big garment factory on the Madurai road. He is their Accounts Manager. He says the job's a really nice one.'

Neha was relieved to hear this, but she was too used to her father to be totally comforted by the news. In any case this is how it always started. Her father's name was Ramachandran and he was the sweetest, gentlest, most loving father any child could wish to have. He always set off for a new job with great enthusiasm and everybody would be happy. He bought Neha a new toy, or a new dress and hummed as he went about his work. But within a few weeks he would begin to look less cheerful. Then he would begin to explain to Neha's mother how someone or the other at his office was too dominating, or dishonest and this was where their problems would begin again. If Neha's father's troubles at office had not been sorted out some days later, he would take the extreme step of resigning from work, or worse, would be relieved from it. And this would send her mother into a scolding, slapping frenzy, impatient with Neha's tiniest error.

Neha devoutly hoped her father would stay long at this new job. She decided she would ask Murthy Gurukal, the temple priest, to send special prayers from her to Ganesha.

The Ganesha temple was on her way home from school. Neha often stopped by for special prayers. The priest was an elderly, immensely kind and wise man named Murthy Gurukal.

Neha finished her snack and told her mother she was going to the temple. 'Come back in time to finish all your homework,' her mother told her. 'Don't spend all evening with your elephant friend.'

'I won't,' promised Neha, shaking her head, with its two tight plaits, for emphasis. Then she skipped out, retracing her steps the way she had come home from the school bus stop.

Her neighbour, Mrs Anandi was very fond of the little girl and liked to offer her tasty treats like banana *appams*. Today she called out to Neha to come and have some idlis. Neha thanked her but refused.

Beside the road there was a gypsy with a large cloth bag and he offered to show Neha a king mongoose fight a snake. She felt slightly scared and fled.

Shakti the temple elephant was blessing a family of visitors to the temple when Neha walked in through the tall temple gates. The elephant's small brown eyes followed the figure of the little girl even as it raised its trunk and accepted the offerings of coins that the visitors were placing in its trunk. Shakti was truly fond of her little friend.

Inside, Murthy Gurukal, the temple priest was handing out flowers and holy ash to the worshippers who stood before the silver covered idol of Lord Ganesha. When he saw Neha, he nodded and smiled in welcome. She folded her hands in prayer and walked slowly behind the other worshippers, waiting for her turn to cup her hands above the flame of the '*aarti*' lamp. When she reached close to the priest, he said, 'Any special requests today?'

'Yes, please,' said Neha, a little breathlessly. 'My father's got a new job and this time I want to ask Pillaiyar to let him keep it a long, long time.' She called Lord Ganesha by the loving name which

people in Tamil Nadu use for him, Pillaiyar, or the child of Shiva and Parvati.

Murthy Gurukal nodded his head gravely. He had communicated this special prayer for Neha before, but he did not remind her of it. He valued his place as Neha's special messenger to God. 'Just sit for a while and pray. Then go home and don't forget to say bye to Shakti before you go,' he said. Then he placed his hand on Neha's head.

She felt happier at once. Now she did not have to worry. Murthy Gurukal and Pillaiyar would look after all her problems she was sure.

'Any person with average
intelligence can master the science
of mathematics.'

— Shakuntala Devi

2

Letters to Lord Ganesha

In the weeks that followed it did seem to look as if Ganesha had given due weight to Neha's prayers. Her father settled down and still came home cheerful. Neha began to think the danger period was passing, that this time her father would not find anyone in his office that he could not stand another minute. Her mother began making something tasty every other day when Neha was back from school, and life would have turned truly rosy if something else hadn't gone wrong.

Neha, who had always been good at Maths, now began to dread the subject. The new teacher ridiculed her mercilessly and humiliated her regularly in class. It all came to a stage where she began to hate numbers and feel that they hated her. She plumbed the depths when she scored only three out

of twenty marks in a test. She felt utterly crushed when her mother wailed, 'Why did this family where we worship Saraswati have to have a child like you?'

'What's happened to me, why can't I be any good at Maths?' wondered Neha as she lay in the dark. The streetlight threw a patch of light on Neha's bedroom wall and a calendar, depicting a picture of Goddess Saraswati on it, fluttered in a small current of breeze. Neha's attention was drawn to the calendar. 'O Goddess Saraswati, you are supposed to help us learn our lessons. Then why have you left me to be laughed at by everybody? Why have you made me so poor at numbers?' Neha's silent cry was accompanied by fresh tears. The serene face of the Goddess on the calendar glowed in the dimness of the room, but brought no answer to Neha's anguish.

She thought of Lord Ganesha in the temple and Murthy Gurukal. The priest was away at his son's home in Trichy and was expected only after another week. 'How will I wait so long for my prayers to reach Ganesha?' thought Neha. 'I will have to write a letter and give it to postman Balu Uncle.'

* * *

On one or two occasions in the past, when things had got too much for Neha, she had written letters to Lord Ganesha and put them in the big red post box, at the corner of her street. The letters carried no stamps, but had her name on the back: Neha Ramachandran. One day, as she was walking back from the school bus stop, a postman on a bicycle, with a bag full of letters slung at the back, stopped and spoke to her.

'Excuse me, but are you Neha Ramachandran?' he asked her.

'Yes, I am. Why?' asked Neha surprised.

The postman smiled, then folded his hands in a *namaste* to Neha. 'I am happy to meet you. It is I who takes your letters to Lord Ganesha,' he said.

'Really?' Neha was most interested. 'What does He say?'

'Oh! He says He has His eye firmly fixed on you and you must not worry, because He will always protect you,' said the postman.

'Did He really say that?' asked Neha with shining eyes.

'Not only did He say that, but He also asked me to bring your letters whenever you needed to talk to Him. So give me your letters directly — you don't even need to put them in the box. I pass this way everyday at this time. Just pop your letter into my bag!' said the postman. Then he was gone with a cheery wave.

That is how postman Balu became one of Neha's friends and she thought of him now, as tears still flowed out of the sides of her eyes on to her pillow.

'I will get up really early tomorrow and write that letter to Lord Ganesha,' thought Neha. 'If I put on the light again, *Amma* may come to investigate.' Thinking thus, she at last allowed herself to sink into sleep.

* * *

The next morning however, it was not the memory of writing the letter that woke Neha up in the early hours. It was the sound of her father humming to

himself as he searched for something in the wooden
shelves that were attached to a wall of Neha's room.

'What are you doing *Appa*?' she asked sleepily.

'Oh the princess has already woken up, has
she?' said her father, coming over to the bed to give
Neha a hug and pat her head. Neha hugged him
back. 'What are you searching for?' she asked him.

'I am looking for a notebook that I had in the
last but one job of mine. Do you remember? The
blue one with leather binding?' asked her father.
Neha shook her head in a 'No.'

'I had some excellent notes in there about
cutting manufacturing costs. I feel these will be useful
in our factory and want to show it to my boss. I am

sorry if my rummaging around woke you up,' said her father with a smile.

'It's all right,' said Neha, smiling back. 'I too needed to get up early to do some work.'

Her father widened his eyes. 'Very important work, huh?' he asked.

'Yes, very,' agreed Neha, giggling. Then her face turned sad. '*Appa*, I am doing so horribly at Maths. *Amma* is always angry and I feel as if numbers hate me and I hate them.'

'Don't worry about *Amma*,' said her father. 'She loves you very much and wants you to do well. As for numbers, they hate nobody and nobody can afford to hate them. Why, everywhere you look there is fun with numbers.'

'How?' demanded Neha.

'I will tell you,' said her father, suddenly thrusting out his jaw in the manner of one of their neighbours, Mrs. Srinivasan. 'Who put these broken flower pots in front of my house?' he demanded in a grating voice that was an exact imitation of Mrs. Srinivasan. He brought his face really close to Neha's. 'See my chin? How many hairs do I have on the wart on my chin?'

'Three!' squealed Neha, collapsing on the bed laughing as the picture of their irascible neighbour rose up in her mind. Her father now put his arms akimbo and asked, 'And how many times have I told you not to play cricket in front of my house?'

'A hundred!' shouted Neha, laughing some more.

'See!' her father said, putting out his hand like a satisfied professor having proved his point. 'You know all the numbers!'

Neha's mother put her head in the door and asked, 'What's all the early morning hilarity about? You two are making quite a lot of noise.'

'Just searching for a notebook,' said her father. Neha's mother looked at both of them, then shrugged her shoulders and walked on. She was really too busy in the morning to have much time for fun and games.

After she had gone, Neha and her father looked at each other. '*Appa*, I'm serious. I'm really having a lot of trouble in school. I can't understand numbers at all anymore,' said Neha.

'You were always a good student, Neha. And remember, numbers are not your enemy. Don't let your fear of numbers defeat you into falling back in class,' said her father, also turning serious. Then he patted her cheek and left the room.

Neha sighed and got out of bed. She prepared to draw the white powder *kolam* in the space in front of their front door. She loved drawing *rangoli* or *kolam* patterns and had several of them in her exercise books too.

Neha may draw the anger of Ms. Eswaran for her stumbling against the mysteries of school sums, but she rarely forgot a *kolam* pattern, even one involving hundreds of dots.

Soon Neha was sprinkling water and smoothing the wet patch of concrete to draw her *kolam* design for the day. She drew a quick, free hand one today, because she still had to write the letter to Lord Ganesha.

'Good morning, Seenu *Mama*,' said Neha, as the milkman paused to look down and admire her *kolam*. 'Are your cows all doing well today? How is Tilottama *Mami*?'

'She is well and so are the cows. Neha, we may be becoming grandparents again,' said the milkman with a smile. He meant that one of his cows would soon have a calf. He glanced down and said, 'This *kolam* reminds me of one my own mother used to do. You have a lovely, steady hand, Neha.'

'Thanks, *Mama*,' said Neha with a rush of happiness. She waved enthusiastically to him as he sputtered out of sight on the moped. Then she turned to go inside, collecting the little pot of *kolam* powder. She must hurry if she had to complete her letter before the runaround for school.

She went and sat at her study table, took a sheet of notebook paper and began to write, 'Dear Lord Ganesha...'

Her mother peeped in again into the room and saw her writing seriously. She shook her head and walked away again. 'When will that child learn to complete all her school work the previous day?' she thought to herself. 'Why does she leave it to the last minute to do her homework?' Aloud, she called to Neha, 'Go for your bath soon, Neha or you will be late for your school bus again!'

'Yes, *Amma*! Just going!' Neha called back. She hurriedly finished her letter and folded it to give it to postman Balu that afternoon.

Then she plunged into the preparations that made every schoolday morning a blur.

'It is important to approach Maths
only in a spirit of curiosity and
discovery...'

— Shakuntala Devi

3

In the Maths Room

Everything seemed to distract Neha as she prepared to leave for school — be it a scraggy-necked chick crow, a new papaya fruit, roadside puppies or a lovely *kolam* design. They all conspired to make her late for the school bus, so that she would have to sprint down the lane to take her seat by her friend.

'Thank you, Ramaswamy *Mama*', Neha would call out to the patient school bus driver. 'Its OK Neha,' he would reply. 'One of these days you are going to trip over your shoe lace as you run.'

But Neha would be already deep in excited chatter with her friend. She usually went to school in a cheerful enough mood. It was as the day wore on and the Maths period came inexorably along to puncture her confidence, that she began to droop dispiritedly.

The high, cruel voice of Ms. Eswaran interfered with any coherent thought that Neha was having. 'If it takes twelve men to do a piece of work in five days, how long will it take seven men to do the same work? Neha, would you like to come and do the problem on the board?'

Neha stood up, temporarily struck dumb. She awkwardly plaited the fingers of her hands together. Finally she managed a very softly mumbled, 'No Miss,' while children around her sniggered and stifled laughs. 'Such a simple problem!' exclaimed Ms. Eswaran. 'Really Neha, is there nothing you can do in Maths? How did you reach this far?'

Rajan put up his hand and received an approving nod from Ms. Eswaran. He swaggered to the board and began to write, 'Number of men = 12' in an untidy scrawl. The class got on with solving the problem, but Neha was unable to shake off the paralysis that seemed to come upon her everytime Ms. Eswaran singled her out for sarcasm and humiliation.

* * *

All year Neha looked forward to the Annual School Day when students from all the classes performed plays, dances, songs and speeches on stage for their parents. It was usually a grand occasion marked by gaiety, very well attended not only by parents, but also grandparents and other family members. Neha's school followed the principle of 'compulsory participation' and every child was given an opportunity to go on stage. For some children, this only meant singing a song in a group. But for Neha, this was one occasion when her individual talent really shone.

The main reason for this was the loving attention Neha received from the music and dance teacher in her school. This was Ms. Nandini, who was a very popular and cheerful person. She had a sweet voice and was young and slim. Most importantly, she loved music and dance and children in equal measure, so she could usually be depended upon to be more patient with the children's mistakes than other teachers.

This year Neha was dancing a leading part in a dance drama marked by beautiful costumes and music. She was to play Krishna in the Radha-Krishna story enthusiastically enacted by a large group of student dancers and singers. What made the event even more pleasurable was that she was being partnered in the dance by her best friend Jyoti, who had been chosen to play Radha. Rehearsals for the School Day event were the high point of Neha's life in school in these weeks. Her dance as Krishna was being much appreciated, with Ms. Nandini daily encouraging her with warm words and suggestions to add some further touches that enhanced its appeal.

As if to balance the happy anticipation of School Day, there was also another event coming up that Neha truly dreaded. An important twenty-five marks Maths Test was coming up to test all their recent concepts in Maths. With her current understanding of numbers touching an all-time low and her confidence at ground level, Neha did not know how she was going to get good marks in this test. As it is, after her last poor showing, Ms. Eswaran had succeeded in dragging her parents to school to meet the Principal. Neha shuddered when she thought of that meeting.

Her parents sat in front of the Principal at his large desk in the slightly gloomy room of his office. Her father was trying to keep a neutral expression on his face, while her mother looked very worried. Neha was called out of her class and escorted by the peon to the Principal's office, which she entered with her heart thudding with fear. The Principal, Mr. Guhan, who had wavy grey hair and wore rimless spectacles, put a hand on Neha's shoulder. He drew her closer to him, to stand next to his desk. Neha knew he meant to be kind, but somehow, this only increased her nervousness, making her so afraid that she was unable to take a breath for a moment or two.

Though the Principal tried to discover the cause behind Neha's poor showing, she quite lost her tongue as soon as she espied Ms Eswaran also standing in the room.

In vain did the Principal try to draw her out and ask her some more questions. In vain did her mother lean forward and say, 'Speak, Neha,' in a voice that held both desperation and command. Neha just could not say anything. Finally, the Principal rang the bell on his desk and asked her to be taken back to class.

As she was marched back along the winding corridors of the school, Neha felt an overwhelming wave of despair sweep over her. 'Is there no way out of this horror of numbers? Must all my school years be tainted with the stamp of failure?'

It seemed as if the only time Neha could get relief from her Maths-related problems was when she could lose herself in the preparations for School Day. She was in fact excelling in her dance, which her classmates began to notice and remark on. It seemed as if Neha's natural love for dance and music was being given the chance to flower fully and was growing stronger as a result.

* * *

Just a couple of days after the encounter with the Principal something awful happened. Neha's class was called to the Maths Room one day, instead of having their Maths lesson in the usual way in their classroom. They walked to the special Maths room in orderly lines, with just the minimum scuffling and giggling to betray the fact that they were children. Ms. Eswaran was not in the room. She must have been busy supervising some class or the other for the School Day festivities. Neha and her classmates were delighted. They hoped Ms. Eswaran would be too busy to come at all!

The charts, models and glass cupboards full of geometric shapes made the Maths Room quite a fascinating place. It was a quiet and orderly room —

Ms. Eswaran's special domain. For the first few minutes, the children sat quietly, expecting Ms. Eswaran to turn up any moment. Then they began talking animatedly, till the Class Monitor Srinidhi reminded them of the possibility of their noise attracting some teacher's attention. A hush fell for a few moments — no child in the class relished the prospect of getting caught by the Principal for making too much noise. It was Murali who thought of Neha doing a dance for the class.

'I have the famous song "*Krishna begane baro...*" cassette with me right now!' he said. 'Miss uses my two-in-one tape recorder for rehearsals. Let's put the tape on and you can dance to it Neha!'

Neha hesitated. 'Won't that be making noise too?' she asked.

'Not as much as everyone talking all at once,' said Srinidhi. 'Go ahead Neha!'

Moments later the sweet strains of the devotional song began to fill the room and Neha began to dance before her classmates. When the heat of the *Mridangam* began in the song, Murali began playing percussion too — on the desks of the Maths Room.

Completely rapt in the song and the movements that went with the sweetly evocative lyrics, Neha danced on and her classmates sat in an appreciative circle around her. The spell would have stayed unbroken if something else had not happened.

A figure swooped into the room and a series of sharp slaps rained on the back and shoulders of a completely stunned Neha. 'Wretched girl! This is what you do and encourage your classmates to do! Sing and dance when you cannot solve a single sum in class. No wonder you are so lacking in any application to studies, Neha. It seems as if your head is only full of foolish and vain ideas. Do you think you will become a film star? Even that needs some brains, you know!' Ms. Eswaran was so furious that her words were coming out in a steady, angry stream. Faced by this barrage of accusation, Neha stared up at her mutely.

Ms. Eswaran's shoulders were shaking with fury. She looked as if she had taken leave of her senses in her anger. Now she pounced on Neha again and held her by the shoulders. She shook Neha so hard that the poor girl was afraid her teeth would fall out of her head. 'How dare you convert the Maths Room into a disco? Have you no respect for studies? This time the Principal shall know about your antics and I shall recommend that you be thrown out of school!' Neha turned white with fear at the teacher's dire threat.

Neha's classmates stood in a stunned silence, not knowing how to deal with the demented fury of Ms. Eswaran, whom they had never seen in such a state. But not all of them were cowed. Unnoticed by anyone, a small boy had already run out of the class and was making his way now to the room where Ms. Nandini was taking a Music class.

Murali burst into the room, uncaring about the others seated there.

'Miss, come quickly!' said Murali breathlessly. 'Maths Miss is hitting Neha for dancing to the Krishna song!'

'Astronomy, music, even natural phenomena, reinforce the mathematical nature of the universe.'

— Shakuntala Devi

4
Music and Mathematics

'Excuse me!' Ms. Eswaran was unprepared for the voice which suddenly sounded at her shoulder as she continued to berate Neha. It was Ms. Nandini and for once her sweet, loving tones sounded very firm, even angry. Ms. Eswaran turned around and looked in some surprise at the Music teacher. She wondered what this younger teacher, junior to her in the school hierarchy, suddenly had to say.

'Madam, have you just been punishing Neha Ramachandran for dancing to a song that is a part of our school function?' asked Ms. Nandini.

Ms. Eswaran was quite surprised to be challenged, but she recovered quickly. 'Do you call it "preparing for a school function" to be shamelessly dancing in the Maths Room? Can't the time be better used to study? In case you are not aware, Neha is a very troublesome student. Her grasp of Maths is non-existent and her head is too full of fanciful ideas to allow her to work hard. She had to be told some truths!' The Maths teacher's voice was turning louder and more harsh.

'What kind of truths are they that destroy a child's confidence and deny her talent?' asked Ms. Nandini in a voice quivering with anger.

'Why are you making such a fuss?' asked Ms. Eswaran, with a false smile, as if she was being very reasonable and Ms. Nandini just the opposite. 'Surely I have the right to deal with my students in the way I choose. I know the capacity of your "talented" Neha. She has yet to cross single digits in any of the tests I have given her.' Ms. Eswaran could not help a certain triumph creeping into her voice.

'If you are unable to see any talent in her, perhaps there is something wrong with your own approach. Have you considered that?' countered Ms. Nandini, without seeming in the least frightened or cowed down by Ms. Eswaran's assertions. 'I myself refuse to believe that any child who has such a strong grasp of *taala*, the rhythm that is the basis of music, can be bad in mathematics!' said Ms. Nandini.

'What connection does her bad performance in Maths have with dancing and singing like an actress?' asked Ms. Eswaran in an outraged voice.

'Why, everything!' said Ms. Nandini. 'All music requires some mathematical application. The scale of the notes, the different beats, the variations in pitch and the faster or slower tempo of singing or playing a song — everything is mathematical. Without maths, a musician would be lost, not even knowing where to enter in a  song whose beat a *tabla* or *mridangam* player is playing. As for Neha, she is perfect in her cues — both in music and dance. You should see the way she can set even Murali right on occasion, when he is playing the *mridangam* for her dance. That child has mathematics in her blood!'

'Next you will be saying that every musician can be a mathematician,' said Ms. Eswaran, sarcastically.

'I am not saying that, but if you only paid more attention to music and dance you would understand the vital connection between these arts and your precious Maths,' said Ms. Nandini in an exasperated way.

'Very well,' said Ms. Eswaran. 'I am ready for a demonstration. Show me how Maths can help music and vice versa.' She folded her arms and stood in an ostensibly attentive manner.

Unfazed by Ms. Eswaran's mocking manner, Ms. Nandini said, 'Look, take *Aadi taala*, the most popular *taala* in Carnatic music. This consists of eight beats. Each beat is called an *akshara*. Each *akshara* has four sub-divisions. These are known as *mathras*. So how many such *mathras* would there be in *Aadi taala*?'

'Thirty two,' said Ms. Eswaran promptly.

'Now when any singer is singing the imaginative portion of a concert, what are known as the *Kalpana swaram*, or any *mridangam* player is playing the solo percussion portion, or any dancer is dancing a *gathi* in this *Aadi taala*, they have to do it in the framework of 32, or multiples of 32. Listen,' said Ms. Nandini. She readied herself to demonstrate the beat of the song she was about to sing, with the fingers of one hand tapping out the beat on the palm of the other. '*Sa-aa-din-cha-ne-ey, O-O- Manasa-a, saaa-din-cha-ney*' sang Ms. Nandini out loud. After a few lines, Ms. Eswaran nodded, as if in understanding.

'It seems simple enough up to now, doesn't it?' asked Ms. Nandini. 'That is because the *mathras* or sub-divisions for each beat are four in number. But the *taala* has several variations, which give it a different character. When an *akshara* is divided into 3 *mathras*, it is known as *Tisra Gathi*, 4 is *Chaturasra Gathi*, 5 is *Khanda Gathi*, 7 is *Misra Gathi* and 9 is *Sankeerna Gathi*. Multiplication and division, that too mental, is an intrinsic part of adjusting to the *taala* and singing or dancing to a song. Neha never disappoints me. She always understands the beat. How could that be possible without an understanding of the Maths behind the music?'

'Singing a song is just a matter of learning it,' said Ms. Eswaran. 'It seems she cannot learn the qualities of numbers in the same way. Maybe the great musicians can come down to teach her,' said Ms. Eswaran, continuing in her sarcastic manner.

Ms. Nandini looked pityingly at Ms. Eswaran. 'You are right without knowing it,' she said. 'The greatest musicians must all have been mathematical geniuses — from Beethoven to Thyagaraja. Else how could they have composed their brilliant music that has survived for centuries? And it is not a coincidence that modern day mathematicians like Albert Einstein were such lovers of music. Those who know this have wisely said, "Maths is the foundation, Music is the structure and Dance the superstructure." Give the child a little more credit for her obvious talent and she could well surprise you.'

'I will give her more credit for anything the day she begins to show some results,' replied Ms. Eswaran tartly. Ms. Nandini shook her head and turned to leave the Maths Room.

As she walked away, she remembered something, and looked back. 'Please return the tape of the Krishna song to Murali at once!' she said. 'It is urgently needed for us to prepare for School Day.'

'Very well,' said Ms. Eswaran in a tight-lipped manner. For some reason, she was staring at Neha as she spoke. And her gaze seemed full of venom to the poor, terrified Neha.

News of the two teachers' argument — what some boys gleefully referred to as a 'jolly good fight' — spread like wildfire throughout the school. It was also common knowledge that Neha was the cause, though some said it was poor Murali! Neha's class was shocked and alarmed by the whole incident. As she sat stunned even some periods later, she could hear her classmates discussing it in different ways.

'How can a teacher be so cruel and unjust?' asked Jyoti and some other of Neha's friends.

'Just because Neha does not like Maths Miss, and she does not like Neha is no reason for our whole class to get a bad name,' declared Rajan and Neha could hear some other children murmur agreement with him.

'Neha, go and say "Sorry, Miss" so she will not be angry with all of us again,' said some of the more timid children. Neha turned and looked at them with big, tear-stained eyes. They wanted her to go and apologise to Maths Miss? What had she done wrong and how had it got her in such a mess?

The whole incident settled like a dark cloud on the pleasurable anticipation of the approaching School Day for Neha. She walked home that evening with bowed head and drooping shoulders. Her misery was so evident that the neighbourhood milkman, passing Neha by on his moped, called out and asked, 'Neha, why the sad face?' She turned and waved at him, but without her usual enthusiasm. Seenu paused a minute in the middle of the road. 'We have a new brown and white calf, Neha!' he told her. 'Come and see it sometime. As it is, my wife's been asking about you.'

Neha smiled at the mention of the calf. 'I will come one day, Seenu *Mama*,' she promised.

'Make it soon!' said the milkman. Then he turned and sputtered away on his moped.

A few steps later, Neha heard Mrs. Anandi call out, 'Cheer up, Neha!' She looked up and saw her neighbour looking at her out of a window. Neha gave a wan smile to acknowledge Mrs. Anandi's greeting, but continued to walk home with slow and dispirited steps. She just wanted to reach home and complete the evening ritual of homework as soon as she could.

In one hour's time she was accompanying her mother to the temple, getting blessed by Shakti. Her mother did not notice her unusual silence, nor did she see the look of understanding pass between her daughter and the temple priest, who gave Neha a specially encouraging smile and a pat on the head along with the flowers and holy ash from Pillaiyar. When her mother was around, Neha did not ask Murthy Gurukal to convey special prayers.

Those were reserved for emergencies. Even if Neha felt the present circumstances were such, she could do little right now, except gaze beseechingly up at Lord Ganesha, who had promised that He was keeping His eye on her.

She devoutly hoped postman Balu had been telling the truth.

5

The Disastrous Zero

The dancing incident seemed to have made Ms. Eswaran keep a sharper eye than ever on Neha. She looked for every opportunity to pounce on the smallest mistake Neha made, and her Maths notebook began to be blotched with the angry red marks of the teacher's corrections.

A week after the incident, School Day was finally held, with the school auditorium acquiring a truly festive air, and crowds of costumed and excited children being herded by their teachers to and from the stage, where they put up a grand show for their parents, grandparents and even aunts and uncles! School Day attracted a big crowd and Neha was one of the lucky children for whom it was an unqualified success.

She loved everything about the day — from the colourful costume she wore as Krishna, with a peacock feather tucked into the yellow cloth that was tied in a small turban around her head, to the carefully applied make-up that she was afraid of ruining by laughing or eating before her event, the hundreds of appreciative faces stretching before her when she was finally on the stage, and then the sheer happiness of going through her dance movements with aplomb.

Murali was looking the part of a true-blue musician, wearing a white *dhoti* and *khadi kurta*, with a long *tilak* on his forehead. Jyoti was resplendent as Radha and she too twirled in her *ghagra-choli* with great gusto, while her eyes kept searching in the audience for her parents. Neha had spotted her mother and father early on in the third row and she could bring them much satisfaction. In the first row, Neha had also spotted the bespectacled face of Mr. Guhan, the school Principal. Today, he too looked happy, the serious features of his face softened into a kind expression.

The thunderous applause that greeted the end of the dance-drama told Neha that the performance had been one of the highlights of the evening. A crowd of fellow students, teachers and some parents came towards them to offer congratulations. But for Neha, the sweetest words came from Ms. Nandini. As Neha walked back to the classrooms along with

the others where they would remove their make-up and get into ordinary clothes, Ms. Nandini slipped an arm across her shoulders. 'You did very well, Neha,' she said. 'Don't let anyone put out that spark which makes you shine so bright! You are not only talented, you are prepared to work hard too. You deserve the best.'

Neha was touched. There could be no mistaking Ms. Nandini's reference to the Maths Room incident. She was grateful that Ms. Nandini believed in her. Then the teacher patted her head and the moment became lost in the general bustle.

There was, however, no let up in Ms Eswaran's hostility.

Neha sat for three evenings with her father to prepare specially for the twenty five mark test. It was important for her to prove herself and try to get into Ms. Eswaran's good books.

As her father sat with her at the dining table, giving her ample time to do each problem, gently correcting her mistakes in calculation, then letting her go ahead with the rest of the sum, Neha felt much better. At the end of the third evening her father was moved to declare, 'You shall do well this time, princess! You understand everything. Just remember to show all the steps correctly, and check the calculations you have made in the margin before handing in your test paper.'

Her mother Lakshmi was frying *papads* or *appalams* for their dinner when she heard this. 'Does the girl really understand?' she asked, with some doubt, coming to the door of the kitchen. 'You always say everything is fine,' she said accusingly to Neha's father. 'Then we find out it really isn't.'

'No, no, this time Neha will do well,' promised Neha's father. 'There's no reason why she should not. She does understand the problems.' He smiled encouragingly at Neha as he spoke.

Neha smiled back but she was far from feeling confident. After all, that was the problem with numbers wasn't it? They seemed to be one thing when she was with her father, and changed completely when she was under the sharp and critical eye of her Maths teacher. What did tomorrow hold for her? How would she do the test?

'All ready for the Maths test?' Jyoti asked. Neha nodded. 'My father spent a lot of time getting me prepared,' she said. Jyoti squeezed Neha's hand in both of hers.

Neha's class went to the Maths Room to write the test, as Ms. Eswaran was administering another test to Class VIII at the same time, and she had arranged the children from the lower class to sit next to their older schoolmates.

Neha took her seat and found her hands were already trembling. She had been upset at the sight of the Maths Room, which she was entering for the first time after the incident of the dance and the severe beating and tongue-lashing she had received from Ms. Eswaran.

A smiling-faced boy from Class VIII, whom Neha remembered as Aditya, who was in the school cricket team was sitting next to Neha. He noticed her pale face and nervous mannerisms. 'Loosen up!' he said. 'It's only a Maths test!'

Neha smiled but said nothing. How could she explain to him how 'only a Maths test' could produce such fear and nervousness in her? She carefully arranged her pencil, eraser, ruler, pen... Checking everything for the umpteenth time would take her away from those terrible scenes...

In a few more minutes the test paper was in front of her, and the familiar sensation of fear and helplessness was settling in her stomach. She began solving the problems but got stuck in the very first one, till Aditya, seeing her sitting immobile, whispered, 'First convert the mixed fractions into improper fractions, then begin the multiplication.'

Gratefully, Neha gathered herself and had barely written two steps when a shadow over her paper made her sense the presence of Ms. Eswaran standing behind her. She turned and looked up with the expression of a terrified rabbit. 'Come on, Neha, write, continue,' said Ms. Eswaran in a voice of false sweetness, while a menacing smile played about her lips. Neha was overcome by fear. 'She wants me to do badly,' her mind was saying. 'She is waiting to show me up as a bad student and get me thrown out of the school,' she thought further. Even after Ms. Eswaran had moved away with a very audible sigh, Neha could not return to normal.

The rest of the paper passed in a muddle. Through her misery and struggles with the problems, Neha was aware of Aditya's concern. He whispered hints to her in several places and looked worried at her fear and paralysis before the Maths teacher. But what could he do? He had his own paper to finish too and he could not spend too much time on Neha's problems, lest he be unable to complete his own test.

The bell rang and Neha's paper was collected without her having attempted two of the problems set in the paper. When Neha told this to Jyoti later, she looked worried. 'You must never leave any portion of the paper unanswered Neha,' her friend told her. 'As it is, even out of the portions you have answered, some marks may be cut if a step has been missed, or a calculation done wrong. If you don't attempt some questions you are really running the risk of getting very low marks,' said Jyoti.

'But what could I do? Maths Miss came and stood at my elbow when I had just started writing and I just could not think properly after that,' said Neha. She was already filled with dread about what her marks in the test would be.

She did not have long to wait. The very next day, Ms. Eswaran came to their class with a grim expression on her face. The answer papers from the previous day were visible to the class, arranged in a sheaf on top of some books in Ms. Eswaran's hand.

'Quite a few of you have disappointed me this time,' began Ms. Eswaran. 'I had expected better efforts from the class. After all, this is only a preparatory test for your forthcoming half-yearly exams.' Neha was fidgeting with nervousness during this speech. Had others in the class done badly too? Then maybe she need not feel so bad. Her shoulders relaxed slightly.

'...there is one person however, who does not disappoint me,' Ms. Eswaran's high-pitched voice was continuing. 'She is completely predictable in test after test, producing results that can only be measured from the bottom, never the top.'

Neha turned pale. She felt the skin on the back of her neck prickle with alarm. Could it be that Maths Miss was talking about her? 'I am talking about Neha Ramachandran,' said the teacher loudly. 'This time she has surpassed herself. Neha has scored zero in a twenty five mark test!' Saying this, Ms. Eswaran held up Neha's paper, with a big, red '0' clearly visible on the top. The class gasped and turned to look at her. Neha wished she could disappear. Why was Miss announcing her marks like this? Why could she not just take her paper and crawl away to a dark corner?

She walked up to collect her paper and took it with trembling fingers. 'All your dancing and singing has made you a big 'Zero'!' Ms. Eswaran hissed at her. Neha was utterly devastated. How was she going to explain this to her mother, who would rain blows on her and scream about her being from some other family? Worse, how was she to explain to her father who had patiently spent many hours getting her prepared for the test?

As her eyes blurred over with tears, the '0' on the paper seemed to look bigger and more mocking than ever. Could things get worse than this?

But it seemed they could, for, minutes after Ms. Eswaran had left the classroom, Neha's old foe Rajan took up the chant, 'Zero! Zero! Neha's got a Zero!' As Neha stared horrified at them, two or three of the boys broke out into a mini-dance  and continued the cry, 'Dummy! Dummy! Neha's a big dummy!' Before Neha's stunned friends could counter with a few shouts of their own, a circle of these boys had formed around Neha and they continued their cruel and unmusical taunting.

It was only the arrival of the Geography teacher for the next lesson that quietened the cruel tormentors.

That evening Neha cried so hard in front of Lord Ganesha and Murthy Gurukal that the elderly priest felt his heart wrung by pity and concern for this child, who was such a regular visitor to his temple.

'I am only a big Zero!' Neha told him tearfully. 'Numbers hate me, the Maths teacher wants me thrown out of school and the children at school tease me all the time. How do I tell *Amma* and *Appa* about my test marks, when I have a big Zero to show them?'

Murthy Gurukal patted her head and asked her to wipe her tear. 'Just sit down,' he told Neha. 'Go, lean on that pillar and just stay for some time. Pillaiyar understands everything. He will set things right. He knows and I know and Shakti knows what a truly intelligent girl you are. Everything will become all right. Just sit here for some time till you feel better, then go and tell your parents.'

But as the evening wore on and he gave out flowers and holy ash to many devotees, without the little figure of Neha moving from her place before the pillar, Murthy Gurukal began to be alarmed. He saw that it was getting dark and it was threatening to rain. So he went up to Neha and said, 'Go home now, Neha. It is getting late and it looks as if it might rain soon. Pillaiyar has understood everything you wanted to tell him — there is no need to wait any more to tell Him everything again. In time, He will take away all these worries. After all, has He not seen to it that your father has kept his present job? Wasn't that the last prayer you had sent up to Him?'

'Yes, it was,' exclaimed Neha, much struck. She felt better at once. Her father showed no sign of getting fed up with this job. Perhaps he really would settle down this time.

'Go home now,' repeated Murthy Gurukal soothingly. 'I would have taken you myself, but I have to stay till it is time to close the temple.'

Reluctantly, not wanting to leave the serene, sheltered haven of the temple, Neha began to walk out of the gates. It was only a short walk to her home, but as she emerged out into the temple courtyard, raindrops had already begun to pelt her skin. By the time she came out on the road, it looked temporarily deserted, as if everyone had taken shelter from the rain, which was now coming down strongly.

For a moment, Neha hesitated, wondering whether to run back into the safety of the temple. Then the approaching darkness made her determined to reach home at once. It was better to reach home quickly and in a wet state, than to reach home after dark even if one's clothes were dry. Her mother would fuss a little, towel her dry and give her a hot drink. But if she reached after dark and began talking about her Maths marks... Neha shivered as she thought of what her mother would do.

Perhaps it was because her head was clouded with all these thoughts that Neha did not notice a lorry coming speeding from the highway that joined the road in front of the temple. At the circle of the roads, where Neha was to turn into the road leading to her home, the lorry swerved around the bend. It was going much too fast to make the turn and it skidded on the wet road. As it careened out of control, its front bumper hit Neha's small figure hurrying on the side of the road.

'Aa-aa-aah!' a startled scream escaped Neha's lips. Then there was silence as her small form lay immobile, where it had been flung by the impact of the lorry.

The truck had screeched to a stop a little ahead. A man jumped out from the seat beside the driver. He sprinted over to Neha, bent over her for a minute, then ran back to the truck.

'It's a small girl, boss!' he said. 'You must have hit her on the turn. She's lying still and there is a bleeding gash on her head. Shall I pick her up?'

The man inside was sweating profusely, even though the air had turned cool with the rain. He ran

his tongue over his lips and rolled his eyes in a way that clearly spelled fear. 'Has anyone seen?' he asked in a voice that came out like a croak. His assistant looked up and down the road. 'No, boss.' he admitted. 'Road's still deserted because of the rain.'

'Then what are you waiting for?' croaked the driver. 'Jump in and let's get out of here.'

'But boss...', the assistant began to speak, before the driver roughly cut him short. 'Forget the heroics,' the older man said. 'Do you understand? I can't have my license taken away from me one more time. Just forget this thing and let's reach where we have to.' As he spoke, he started the truck and left it to idle noisily. His assistant hesitated a few more seconds, then reluctantly climbed into the front of the truck beside the driver. Running away like this when the girl was clearly hurt was bothering him a lot, but what could he do? He was just the driver's assistant and didn't even have a license of his own to drive a truck. He bet he could drive better than this — this killer — if he got the chance.

The young man's thoughts turned darker. He slumped low into his seat as the lorry began moving again, more slowly now that the driver had been shocked by the accident. They drove a few hundred yards, then the assistant suddenly sat bolt upright again, his expression one of frozen horror.

'Stop boss!', he exclaimed out loud and the driver had obeyed him before he heard the next part of his sentence. 'There's an elephant on the road!'

6

One for Success

When the driver's assistant had looked at the rain-swept road, he had been watching for passers-by who may have seen the accident. The circle of three roads was slightly downhill from the Ganesh temple. And as Neha had left the temple courtyard, trying to hurry home in the rain one pair of eyes had noticed her departure — wise, brown eyes that were small in a large, magnificent head.

Shakti, the temple elephant had seen Neha arrive in poor spirits at the temple earlier in the evening. When it began to rain, Muthuraman, her attendant had left her standing at the side of the temple gates where the thatched roof of the shoe and slipper stand gave Shakti shelter from the rain. He himself had gone to warm himself with a cup of coffee in a nearby lane. A light chain tethered Shakti to the trunk of a coconut tree.

Shakti saw Neha leave the temple for home, even though the rain became intense. Her worried eyes followed the small figure. When the truck hit Neha Shakti trumpetted loudly and raised her trunk. This startled some of the shopkeepers and bystanders who were huddling under the eaves of buildings to keep dry.

'Ha-rr-rr-oumph!' yelled Shakti, and everyone was alarmed. 'Where's Muthuraman?' some of them yelled. A boy was sent running to call him to calm Shakti. But by the time the boy had moved just a few feet, there was a loud snapping sound. Shakti had snapped her chain! The temple elephant was now moving purposefully, with great speed, towards the circle where the temple road met the highway.

The driver's assistant in the hit-and-run truck that had struck Neha looked with terrified eyes through the windshield at the huge elephant that blocked their path. 'How did the elephant get here b-b-boss?' he asked, his teeth chattering.

'How do I know?' growled the driver. 'You were supposed to be looking out at the street'.

'But-but...' said the driver's assistant. What else he had to say never became clear, because while he spoke, the elephant had moved close to the truck,

wrenched open the lorry door with its powerful trunk and lifted the young boy bodily out of the truck.

'Aaaah!' yelled the driver's assistant. He was held up in the air for a minute, his arms and legs flailing wildly, then he was roughly thrown to the ground, where a crowd of people, who had come running in pursuit of Shakti, caught hold of him and held him fast. Now the elephant's trunk had moved inside the truck like a probing instrument and Shakti moved as close as she could get to the truck. From here, she twisted her trunk around the driver's neck, while he sat frozen with terror in his seat. His hoarse and strangled cries told the assembled people how he was being choked by the force of Shakti's trunk. Shakti lifted a leg and pushed it against the truck. The whole vehicle rattled. She twisted her trunk some more and the driver came tumbling out on to the ground, unable to shelter in his vehicle any more.

Like his assistant, the driver was held captive by the crowd, but it seemed as if Shakti's fury was far from satisfied. Trumpetting loudly, she pulled a door of the lorry off its hinges with her trunk. She gave the front of the truck several kicks with her large, flat foot, denting it considerably. It was as if she could not forgive the vehicle and its keepers for what they had done to Neha.

And what of Neha? The crowd had not noticed the small shape hidden by the grass and shrubs that lined the road. They had just held the two men from the truck till someone in authority arrived to make sense of what had happened. But now, to their amazement, they saw the enraged elephant move to the side of the road and tenderly pick up a child's form from the ground.

'Aah!' gasped the assembled people. Only now did they understand why the elephant had attacked the occupants of the truck. There must have been an accident. They held the two men tighter and the driver felt his shirt collar closing even more tightly around his bruised, aching neck. He knew there was nothing he could do now except wait for the punishment that was inevitably coming his way.

Shakti walked down the road, carefully holding Neha, and people made way for her. Muthuraman came running up, ready to scold Shakti, but he was quietened by the sight of Shakti and her special burden.

'My God, it's Neha Ramachandran!' exclaimed one of the assembled onlookers. This was Mrs. Anandi's son, Prashant. In a trice, he had run to inform Neha's parents. On the way he passed Seenu the milkman, who almost collided with him. 'What's the matter?' yelled the milkman.

'Neha's had an accident!' called Prashant, continuing to run. 'A truck hit her and the temple elephant is carrying her away!'

'Who's taking her to hospital?' asked the milkman. But he was talking to empty air. Prashant had already run out of sight. Seenu started his moped again, racing to where he could see a crowd moving down the road.

* * *

At first, there was a throbbing pain on the side of her head and she was being carried, gently, but with an unmistakable up and down swing, that told her someone was holding her, someone whose strength was entwined all round her, protecting her from bumps and shocks. Neha relaxed and let herself yield trustingly in this grip and the pain in her head grew less intense.

When she opened her eyes, she was seated on the back of an elephant that was flying through the air! The elephant's broad forehead in front of her reminded her of Shakti. 'Wherever Shakti's taking me must be somewhere good,' thought Neha. She leaned forward and took hold of the elephant's ears and began to enjoy her ride.

The flying elephant made a gentle sweep in the sky and began coming down to green, forested land that stretched as far as Neha's eyes could see. Before they could touch the ground, Neha heard a swishing sound next to her and saw a beautiful fairy come flying close to them. When the elephant touched the ground, Neha let go of its ears and patted the broad forehead.

The elephant kneeled on the ground, while the fairy walked to the front of it and called to Neha. 'Neha! Don't worry,' she called in the gentlest of voices. 'I am here, I will help you. Come, let me show you the wonderful place where you have arrived.'

'Who are you?' asked Neha in wonder. The sweet face and the kind expression on the fairy's face was reminding her of Tilottama, the milkman's wife!

'I am your fairy godmother,' smiled the fairy. 'I had to see that you had a safe journey to the domain of Saraswati, the Goddess of learning. If she blesses you, all your problems will melt away like snow

before the sun. Look! Some baby elephants are beckoning you! Why don't we follow them?'

Neha looked out at green vistas — meadows and fields dotted with flowering bushes and tall, shady trees spreading a canopy of green. In the distance, small animals that looked like goat kids were playing, every few moments they would kick up their heels and skip! When Neha turned her head, she saw to her amazement, a group of baby elephants.

What was astonishing was that these baby elephants were white in colour, unlike any elephants she had seen before. Their skin glowed milky white, with an occasional sheen of pearl, or ivory, or bluish porcelain. When they saw Neha look their way, all the elephants raised their trunks in a salute, as if in welcome. Neha was thrilled.

69

'They have gathered here to greet you, Neha,' spoke the fairy godmother. 'Let us see where they take us.'

Neha and her fairy godmother walked a short way behind the elephants and reached a green glade where a tinkling waterfall, coming down a hillside, made a small pool. Graceful swans swam in the water and on a small island in the centre of the water, Goddess Saraswati sat playing the *veena*! Its divine sound made Neha pause and take an awed breath as she looked upon the beautiful scene in front of her.

The fairy godmother smiled. 'Go to Goddess Saraswati, Neha. She will help you.'

Neha looked at the fairy, unsure of how to make her way across the water. But when she looked again, big lotuses had appeared in a path leading straight up to the Goddess. They opened their petals welcomingly and Neha stepped lightly on each to reach Saraswati.

When Neha stood before her, Saraswati stopped playing the *veena* and looked at Neha. Neha folded her hands and sang, *'Saraswati Namasthubhyam, Varade Kaama Roopini, sarva Vidya Pradayini...'*

The Goddess smiled and asked Neha, 'Who taught you this song?'

'My Music teacher,' said Neha.

'Do you like her?' asked the Goddess.

'Very much,' said Neha. 'She is also beautiful like you. You look so much like her!'

'I see,' said the Goddess. 'I am happy to see you. But why have you come all this way?'

'O *ma* Saraswati, I don't seem to be able to grasp numbers at all,' said Neha in a voice that quivered with tears. 'Because of this, my Maths teacher always shows me down in front of my classmates. My mother too scolds me and slaps me because of my low marks in Maths. She says I bring shame to her family, which has scientists and mathematicians by the dozen.'

'How do you want me to help?' asked Saraswati.

'I have heard that you made an ordinary shepherd boy into the great poet Kalidasa! Will you not help me to become friends with numbers?' asked Neha.

71

'My dear Neha, I am mainly in charge of the performing arts, music, dancing and even literature. I have already blessed you with the gift of music and dancing. If you want friendship with numbers, you should really seek Lord Ganesha's blessings! Pray to him and he will help you as you go around the world of numbers — the Land of Zero!' said Saraswati.

'The Land of Zero?' asked Neha in wonderment. Saraswati laughed softly, her face glowing and her whole personality radiating grace and happiness, 'Yes, you shall have a wonderful time there among the numbers, who love you.'

'Numbers don't love me!' exclaimed Neha. 'They hate me and turn against me and I hate them! If this is the land of numbers, send me back home!'

'You will reach home again, I promise,' said Saraswati. 'But explore the Land of Zero first. Look, the baby elephants are waiting to show you around!'

Neha kneeled before the Goddess. 'Thank you, O Mother,' she said simply.

'Ganesha will help you when you think of him. But you may call upon him only once,' said Saraswati. 'I must warn you. The path through the kingdom of Zero is dangerous. You may face lots of difficulties. It will test your desire to learn numbers. Whatever happens, don't be afraid, your guardian angel is there to help you.' She raised her hand in blessing and farewell.

Neha turned to leave. This time, a boat floated on shore and Neha understood that she must take it. She climbed into the boat and began to paddle with the oar she had found.

* * *

When she reached the other side, her fairy godmother was waiting for her. The baby elephants too waited and as soon as they saw Neha, they raised their trunks and trumpetted in celebration.

The elephants all gathered in a circle and began to dance, while Neha stood entranced in the middle, watching this marvelous sight.

> 'Dear dear Neha, you are here at last,
> Just in time too, the fun is going to start
> All these days, your troubles weighed a ton
> And all because you had not met one!'

sang the elephants, in a sprightly marching tune, while they executed quick steps to their own song.

'One?' said Neha. 'Am I going to meet One?' she began walking along beside the quick stepping elephants, interested inspite of her earlier reservations.

They walked over a raised slope and then downhill, where plenty of flowers spilled their cheerful colours. Neha was amazed to see giant sunflowers, on one of which, a familiar figure sat. When Neha reached him, he jumped down to greet her.

'Hello, Neha! I'm Number One,' he said.

Number One looked very much like Aditya, the friendly boy from her school who had tried to help her in the Maths test! Number One bowed and broke into a song:

'Great times Neha, the fun has just begun —
Happy to meet you, they call me Number One.
I'm small, I'm single, I don't usually mingle,
But in my own way, I'm powerful like the sun!'

'How wonderful to meet you, Adi... I mean, Number One' said Neha breathlessly. 'What do you mean by saying you don't usually mingle?'

'All counting of the whole number world begins with me, Neha,' said Number One. 'My most important quality is that whatever number you multiply by me, or divide by me, you get the same number as the answer. In this way, I leave the number unchanged. See? Multiply 956 by me, what do you get? 956. Or divide 16 by me, what do you get? 16. That's the special quality of 1.'

'I never thought of it that way,' said Neha. 'About leaving the numbers unchanged, I mean. Tell me some more about yourself,' she said.

'Well, my special qualities are known to all. In this universe, the all important God is only One. In all fields of human activity, the best achiever is called Number One. One sun brings light to this world and every journey begins with the first, the most important step!' said Number One. Neha nodded in understanding.

'I am the single most important element in counting,' said Number One. 'Any number which follows another is always 1 more than the previous number, and any number before another is always 1 less. I am also the first and very special Prime. Every other Prime Number is called thus only by seeing whether it is divisible by me and itself.'

'I know this,' nodded Neha.

'Now see, just look at the steps in my multiplication table,' said Number One. He looked down at the green grass carpet they were walking on and Neha received another astonishing surprise. The whole multiplication table of 1 began to appear on the grass in front of them, the numbers glowing bright yellow and scrolling on and on to show Neha a steady stream of multiples of 1!

'Just look at all the multiples Neha,' said Number One. 'They always appear in the sequence of 1 to 9. If the digit of one multiple add up to 5, the digits of the next will add up to 6 and so on. I will show you these secret steps in my multiplication table. Stop!' he said, referring to the scrolling numbers on the grass. They stopped moving at 162 × 1 = 162.

'Now look,' said Number One. 'Add 1 to 6 and 2. The answer is 9. Now took at the next multiple, 163, and add those digits. They add up to 10 and again, add 1 and 0, you get 1. Do you see?' Neha nodded, a little uncertainly.

'You will see it better when you do it yourself,' said Number One. 'Come on, look at the next multiple.'

'164', read Neha. '1 plus 6 plus 4 is equal to... 11. And 1 plus 1 in 11 is 2! I think I have got it. 165 will be equal to 3!' she said, without totaling the digits in the number. 'And 166 will be 4, 167 will be 5...' she continued.

'Exactly,' beamed Number One. 'I am really happy with the time you spent with me. You need to go ahead now, to meet the other numbers and I will accompany you, but just remember one more thing

about me. I am neither a prime number nor am I a composite number. I am just myself — unique Number One.'

'Thanks, Number One,' said Neha, a trifle shyly. 'I won't forget your special qualities.' She felt happy to have met her first friend in the world of numbers, and Number One and her fairy godmother accompanied her to the waiting boat which would take them further upstream to meet Number Two. As Neha sat smiling in the boat, enjoying her ride, a gust of wind suddenly brought a dark shape to their side. Neha looked in the direction of the wind and gasped. She felt a sudden chill. It was her Maths Teacher, who seemed to possess the powers of flying about like a witch!

'So you are trying to understand the mysteries of numbers, are you Neha?' asked the witch-lady. She gave a loud cackling laugh. 'Don't waste the time of these poor Numbers. No magic can teach you Maths, with your head full of song and dance.'

'I am not wasting their time. I am just trying to know them better than I do.' Although she spoke thus, her voice was trembling. It was with great difficulty that she remembered the words of Saraswati Devi not to be afraid. Why should she worry? Her fairy godmother was there to protect her.

'Where are you going now?' asked the witch harshly.

'I am going to see Number Two,' said Neha.

With a horrible cackling laugh, the witch said, 'I will see how you do so!' In the next instant, Neha was terrified to see a huge crocodile rear out of the water with open jaws, coming close to the boat, as if he would overturn it.

'The witch has turned herself into a crocodile!' shouted Number One.

'Here, Neha, take this,' said her fairy godmother, putting a spear in Neha's hand. For a second, Neha looked at the weapon in astonishment. Then she threw it at the crocodile, hitting it in one yellow eye.

In a burst of black and yellow smoke, the crocodile disappeared, while the witch's form could be seen flying away.

Neha began breathing freely again, reassured that she was in no danger. They reached the shore and got off the boat to see the baby elephants waiting for them. The baby elephants frolicked around her and made her laugh. Number One did the occasional cartwheel as they went along. They made a really jolly procession. Neha felt happier than she had felt for a long time.

'Mathematics is the mother of all sciences.'

— Shakuntala Devi

7

Two for Joy

Humming along with the music that seemed to accompany the dancing elephants wherever they went, Neha felt a curious excitement about her next encounter. What would Number Two be like?

A house with two tall chimneys rose ahead of them. There were two identical striped cats sleeping in the sunlight in front of the house. One slept on the gatepost, which had a large numeral '2' shaped somewhat like a duck, carved in stone on it. The cat rested his head under the chest of the '2' to shield its eyes from the sun! Another cat slept on a bench in the garden. As Neha approached the house, she saw there was another bench, just like the first, on the other side of the garden.

'There's two of everything here,' she thought to herself. 'Two chimneys, two cats, two benches.'

As if he was reading her thoughts, Number One said, 'Number Two likes pairs of everything, as you can see.'

'Yoo-hoo! Brother where are you?' called out Number One as they walked to the back of the house, where a rotund figure wearing a track suit was exercising on parallel bars. Seeing them, he jumped down and wiped the sweat from his forehead. Neha smiled to see that he resembled plump Muthuraman, Shakti's keeper!

'Hello Neha, I heard that you were coming,' said Number Two. 'Goddess Saraswati told me to expect you. Pardon my track suit. I have to keep exercising to stay trim. I cannot stay slim at all times, like my brother Number One here!'

They all trooped around to one end of the garden where rows of fruit trees were neatly planted and beds of vegetables grew to one side of the house. In the shade of a tall and leafy mango tree, a large wooden picnic table with benches around it was laid with a wonderful feast. Neha could spot all her favourite thing — cakes, tall jugs of coloured juice, masses of potato wafers, *dahi-vadais*, with dark sweet *chutney* to pour over them, *poories* and *channa* and a whole host of other goodies. The best of all was a towering silver tub of ice cream with a

giant scoop next to it for serving oneself. Neha looked with astonishment at this wonderful ice-cream that showed no signs of melting in the bright sunshine.

'So much food just for you?' asked Neha.

'Yes, I do like to eat,' said Number Two. But as they sat down to eat, Neha had more reason to be amazed. Not only did Number Two like to eat, in an absent-minded way he did not stop when the food was over in his plate — he continued to eat the plate and spoon too! Neha stared and stared.

Number One noticed Neha's surprise and said, 'My brother has many special qualities Neha. Don't get fooled by his tricks. When he stops eating, he will tell you about himself.'

Number Two seemed to start out of his absent-minded spell. Still chewing, he said, 'You are familiar with many Twos, Neha. In Time, there is Day and Night, in life, there is Male and Female. In nature, there is *Prakruthi* and *Purusha* — all these are expressions of me.'

Neha considered his words, while the baby elephants settled themselves under the shade of a nearby tree with a huge mound of fresh fruit and green vegetables in front of them. Even in the shade, their white skin glowed and shone. Neha watched them fascinated. 'How do the elephants stay so beautifully clean?' she asked.

Number Two glanced at the elephants munching happily on their own feast. 'Those are Zero's favourite elephants,' he said. 'Whenever they begin to look a little dusty, he just blows on them or something, I don't exactly know what. And they emerge shiny clean.'

'Can Zero really do that?' asked Neha and Number Two widened his eyes at the question. 'Zero can do anything and everything. This whole kingdom belongs to him and he is the kindest, most just ruler ever seen anywhere. Under him, we numbers always keep our promises and do our duty in all circumstances. Zero teaches us to be completely reliable so that we can always be trusted.

84

After all, great things depend on us — from the smallest machine in a factory to the giant rockets meant to explore outer space — every machine is made with mathematical measurements and all our sister sciences like engineering, or physics, or astronomy depend on numbers to perform their duties.'

'I never thought of numbers as trustworthy,' said Neha. 'They seem to play tricks with me when I write Maths tests in class.'

Both Number One and Number Two gave Neha a sharp look. 'Perhaps something or someone is coming between you and your understanding of the fine qualities of numbers,' Number One finally said. 'Don't worry, your troubles will be at an end when you have met Zero,' he added.

'Come and look at my collection of twins when you have finished eating,' said Number Two and of course at that very moment, Neha felt full enough to get up. To her delight, the last two mouthfuls of cake left on her plate did a smart disappearing act the minute she had decided she had enough. When he saw her looking at her plate in disbelief, Number

Two laughed aloud. 'Another one of Zero's touches. He likes to round things off in his own way!'

Number Two led the way to a cabin at the back of the garden, with two open windows and a big wooden door. Neha was completely charmed with what she saw inside. Number Two's collection of twins was made up of identical pairs of creatures — all kinds of creatures. There were many species of insects. A pair of spotted beetles carefully crawled up a twig kept inside a large glass box, while in the same box with a sandy floor, a pair of dragon flies with green, gauzy wings perched on the edge of a water dish that resembled a pond. In a small wicker basket, a pair of baby squirrels slept snuggled together, noses and tails touching to keep extra cosy. As Neha leaned over them, Number Two said, 'These two are a real handful when their mother arrives to feed them. Don't get deceived by their angelic looks.'

When Neha put her eye to a hole in a cardboard box, four green dots glowing up at her told her that another pair of twins was inside, looking at her with phosphorescent eyes. 'Twin foxes,' explained Number Two. 'They're still too small to sleep out in the light, that's why they're in the box.' He smiled at Neha's wonderment at his collection of creatures. 'My collection is ever changing,' he said, 'Pairs of creatures grow, leave and other ones arrive to take their place. I am not keeping any creature a prisoner here, just letting them know there is a friendly home should they need it.' Neha nodded in understanding. How nice to be able to relate to the world of winged and furred creatures this way.

They emerged into the light outside and Number Two led Neha to a bench where the two of them could sit and dangle their feet. He sang aloud:

> *'Perfect equality is the promise of two*
> *Know me better, and you will know what to do*
> *I'm even, I'm prime, I deal in doubles*
> *With me on your side, you'll have no trouble!'*

The song sounded so nice in Number Two's strong baritone that Neha clapped her hands in appreciation.

'Will that help you to remember that I am the only even prime number in all the numbers?' asked Number Two. 'Yes!' exclaimed Neha, with shining eyes.

'Great, now just remember this too. To multiply any number by me is like adding that number to itself. I am a mirror showing any number its exact self! Thus $651 \times 2 = 651 + 651$! Or 24×2 is...'

'Twenty four plus twenty four, that is forty eight,' said Neha. She really was catching on.

'Good. This is the reason why an equation like $n + n = n \times n = n^2$ is possible only with the number 2,' said Number Two. 'Work it out for yourself.'

'Two plus two is equal to four and two into two is also four, so is two squared,' said Neha in a considering voice. 'Yes, I can see how two is different from any other number.'

'Now look at the multiplication table of two. Do you remember it, or would you like the scrolling steps?'

'I remember it,' said Neha. 'It is very easy. The multiples always end in 2, 4, 6, 8, or zero.'

'Exactly!' said Number Two in a very pleased voice. 'There will be more that you will notice about me as we go along, but now I would like to tell you one very interesting sum.'

'What is it?' asked Neha.

'If you add 123456789 to 123456789, then add 987654321 and 987654321, then a 2 to the whole, you get the beautiful answer, 222222222!' said Number Two with an excited flush on his face.

'Really!' said Neha. She immediately took a twig and began to do the sum in the dusty ground in front of the garden bench. When she got the correct answer, she was thrilled.

$$123456789 + 123456789 +$$
$$987654321 + 987654321 + 2$$
$$= \underline{222222222}$$

'You numbers have many secrets,' she said aloud, looking at Number Two. 'Yes, we do,' said Number Two.

'Thank you for sharing some of your secrets with me,' said Neha.

'Let me accompany you to meet Zero. We will have a wonderful time collecting all my brothers along the way.'

'Let's go,' said Neha, feeling very enthusiastic. The happy procession of Neha and her fairy godmother, with Numbers One and Two had just started walking, when a loud hissing sound was heard. As Neha looked around in puzzlement, a large black cobra emerged from a bush and began to make its way to them.

'The witch has turned into a cobra!' yelled Number Two. In a flash, Number One pulled out a '*been*', a snake-charmer's pipe, out of his pocket and began playing it before the snake to distract it.

'Hiss-ss-ss' went the snake. 'I will see that this wretched girl can go no further. How dare she try to befriend the numbers?'

Neha was cringing in terror. How long would Number One be able to distract the snake with his '*been*'? The snake was swinging from side to side before the pipe, but every now and then, it would try to make a sideways movement towards Neha.

Then the fairy godmother turned into a mongoose! In front of Neha's amazed eyes, she darted at the snake and immediately brought down the reared hood. There was a terrific fight between the snake and the mongoose, till the snake slid speedily away. Neha sighed in relief. 'Thank you, dear guardian angel,' she told her fairy godmother. 'You truly protect me at all times.

8

The Number Game

When Neha reached the home of Number Three, she found a triangular shaped building. A big bronze sculpture in the garden showed the three heads of Brahma, Vishnu and Shiva. A tall trident rose up from the ground in front of the sculpture and on a three-legged throne sat Number Three. His head was tied with a scarf of three colours and three long chains of coloured beads hung down his chest. To her delight, Neha found that he was the gypsy man she had met on the way to the temple!

'Hello, Number Three!' Neha greeted him. 'Was it you who sent us the mongoose to defeat the snake?'

'My dear Neha,' said Number Three. 'My mongoose and snake are both taking a nap. But I am indeed relieved to see you arrive here safely with brothers One and Two. Did you say you met a snake?'

All the four of them began to relate different portions of their eventful journey to Number Three. When they were through, Neha asked him, 'What are you going to tell me about yourself?'

'The world is full of interesting triplets, have you noticed, Neha? Land, water and sky, father, mother and child, sun, moon and earth.'

'Yes, I remember,' said Neha, thinking about the 'three' nature of things.

Something else occurred to her and she said out loud, 'When I go to music class I have to sing a song in three different tempos — first slowly, then a little faster, then much faster.'

'Neha is paying homage to us with her singing and dancing,' said Number Three, to which Number Two added, 'Hear, hear!'

'She may not know it, but she can pick up the division into numbers and even fractions of numbers, in many things she does. Why, her *kolam* designs are usually flawless! She never makes a mistake in the numbers of dots, even though they are in uneven rows like seventeen, fifteen, etc.' said Number Three.

'When you think of triangles, think of me
I'm prime, I'm odd, I'm simply me
Three, six, or nine is all you will see
From the digits of my multiples, endlessly!'

sang Number Three out loud. By now, Neha had wisened up to the ways of the numbers. She did rapid calculations in her head and found,

$3 \times 4 = 12$ (1+2=3),

or $3 \times 6 = 18$ (1+8=9),

or $3 \times 11 = 33$ (3+3=6).

'The digits of the multiples in the multiplication table of Three always add up to 3 or 6 or 9,' said Neha, pleased that she had immediately understood Number Three's song.

'That's right!' said all the numbers. Number Two clapped his hands.

'One more hint,' said Number Three and Neha nodded, all attention now.

'Just remember, every even power of any integer is either a multiple of me or exceeds a multiple of mine by 1. Remember?'

'Every even power of any integer...' said Neha committing it to memory. '...is either a multiple of three, or exceeds a multiple of three by 1. So — 2 raised to four is... 16, and 16 is 1 more than 15, a multiple of... THREE!' she shouted excitedly. It was giving her great pleasure to be able to test out whatever the numbers said, and finding that everything always worked out as they had promised.

Neha set off for her remaining journey in a horse drawn chariot belonging to Number Three, along with the others. She looked forward to accompanying her fairy godmother and the three brothers to meet their fourth, fifth and other brothers. But her mood of happy optimism received another jolt, when the witch came out from behind a tree, where she had been hiding.

Now she suddenly stood in the path of Neha's procession. 'Why do you waste your time with this child? She does not deserve it,' she said.

The Numbers and the fairy stood protectively around Neha. 'Let us pass,' said Number Two. 'We are on our way to meet Zero!'

The witch laughed a scornful laugh. 'Zero?' she asked. 'First tell me how you will get to your next brother!' With these words, she raised one hand and uttered a 'mantra' before bringing it down again. What happened when she brought her hand down made everyone in the procession gasp.

There was the rumble and shaking of an earthquake and in front of the procession, a huge chasm appeared in the earth. The horses of the chariot reared up and began to whinny in fear.

'Oh no! Such a big chasm! How are we ever going to cross it?' said Neha.

'Looks like coming with you is going to prove costly for all of us,' said Number Two.

'What rubbish! Nothing can happen to Numbers. As long as knowledge exists, Numbers will exist,' said Number Three.

'But what are we going to do now?' said Number One.

Neha and the Numbers all looked expectantly at the fairy. She closed her eyes and waved a wand. A magic carpet appeared and began to float down to them. Neha and the Numbers saw it and cheered.

All of them got on to the magic carpet and sent Three's chariot back to his home. They were just about to raise themselves off the ground, when another rumble sounded.

'Quick, let us escape!' said Number Three and pulled up the last corner of the carpet that was still on the ground. Even as they were moving away, huge rocks came hurtling towards them. But everyone of these missed the magic carpet and the relieved group sailed away.

It was in this triumphant mood that Neha moved forward to meet Number Four. They reached Number Four's house, where everything looked square and solid.

Number Four's hair was turning grey, but his smile was brighter than ever. As Neha looked up into his twinkling eyes, she recognised the dear face of Postman Balu, who carried her special letters to Lord Ganesha. She clapped her hands in delight and Number Four lifted her a few feet off the ground, with his hands around her waist.

> 'You must have noticed this before,
>   A house is built with corners four
> North, South, East and West,
>   I'm stable, I give support to the rest!'

sang Number Four and Neha exclaimed excitedly, 'I know that all your multiples end in 4 or 8 or 2 or 6 or 0! I've noticed that when I had to learn the four times table.'

Number Four looked very pleased. 'Have you noticed those steps? Then let me also tell you the Secret Steps!' He leaned down and whispered in Neha's ear.

'The digits of the multiples, if added together, show a pattern of moving down in a descending order', said Neha out loud. '9, 4, 8, 3, 7, 2, 6, 1, 5...

It's like a *kolam* pattern!' Then she wanted to test it. 'Nine into four is thirty six (9×4=36). 3+6=9. That means the next multiple must add up to 4. That's 40! 4+0! Then comes 44, adding up to 8. I know the pattern!'

All the numbers gathered around Neha. The baby elephants blew sharp blasts on their trunks that sounded like the blowing of many trumpets. Neha felt very pleased at so much admiration. What had she worried about? She knew more about numbers than she had ever thought she did.

'Let's go and meet Number Five!' she said. The numbers laughed at her enthusiasm.

While the sound of their laughter was still in the air, another sound began to be heard. It was the hoarse cackling of the witch. She appeared and said, 'So you insist on taking this girl further along the road? You think your magic carpet has solved all your problems? I possess greater magic than that! All the five elements are obedient to me. You may have crossed earth's obstacles, but can you conquer fire?'

The witch raised her hand again and tossed some ashes into the air, uttering a powerful *mantra* as she did so. To Neha's horror, huge flames began leaping around them. There was fire everywhere — it looked as if they would all burn to cinders!

'Help! O fairy godmother, you are my guardian angel, can't you do something?'

'The witch has called the magic carpet to her side,' said Number One. 'O! what are we to do?'

A flying spark fell on Number Two. 'Ouch, ow!' he yelled. 'Somebody get us out of here!'

As they had been speaking, the fairy had her eyes closed and seemed to be praying with great concentration. A huge winged white horse appeared in the sky and swooped down towards them. The horse was so big that all of them could clamber on to its broad back. It flapped its powerful wings and they began flying to safety, leaving the leaping flames behind.

Neha was completely awed by the beautiful horse. 'This is Uchaishravas,' said the fairy. 'Indra himself must have sent him to help us, thanks to the blessings of Saraswati Devi.'

Neha patted the broad back carrying them to the safety of Number Five's domain. She loved Uchaishravas and was very grateful for the help that Saraswati Devi and Indra were giving her.

They reached a house shaped like a pentagon and Neha knew immediately that it belonged to Number Five. As they dismounted from the flying horse, Number Four said to her, 'Remember all the five aspects we keep seeing around us, Neha?'

'Tell me some of them, Uncle Four,' said Neha.

'Five elements can be seen around us, which our ancients called *Panchabhootham*. These are earth, water, fire, wind and sky. Five senses belong to the body — the senses of sight, touch, taste, smell and hearing. The human body itself is a Number Five, with four arms and legs and a head to control them.'

'And five fingers and toes on each hand and foot,' added Neha.

As they walked towards the pentagon house, a familiar sound was heard. Neha heard it and turned immediately. She saw the two-wheeler approaching and said, 'Is it... Yes it is! *Seenu Mama!*' She yelled and waved at the approaching Number Five.

Number Five stopped his bike, got off and executed a small bow. 'I am so happy to see you

Neha,' he said. 'I was waiting for you ever since Saraswati Devi told me that you would be coming. I had gone to invite my brother Number Six. He will be coming shortly. We often play cards together in the afternoon. You will meet him too.' Then he sang,

Just remember, I'm half of ten
I'm prime, 5 and 0 are found at my ends.
If you've understood, the secret of four
Just turn it around for me, no more.'

'What does that mean?' asked Neha, slightly mystified. 'I understand that you are a prime number, and half of ten, but what's this about reversing the secret of four?'

9,4,8,3,7,2,6,1,5 ?
5,1,6,2,7,3,8,4,9 !

Number Five smiled and said, 'Did you learn that the Secret Steps in the Four multiplication table come down 9, 4, 8, 3, 7, 2, 6, 1, 5? Well, in my table, they go up 5, 1, 6, 2, 7, 3, 8, 4, 9!'

'Really?' said Neha. She quickly tested Number Five's secret tip by adding the digits of the multiplication table of 5. It took her only a few seconds to discover that 5, was followed by 10, that is $1+0=1$, followed by 15, that is $1+5=6$...

'5, 1, 6, 2, 7, 3, 8, 4, 9!' she shouted. 'Another secret pattern!'

'By learning the links and patterns within the numbers, you are only strengthening your ability to add and multiply and perform all the maths processes inside your brain! Don't worry anymore about numbers Neha. You are destined to meet King Zero himself.'

'Keep it up, Neha!' chorused Numbers One, Two, Three, Four and Five. Neha was very happy that she had reached this far, inspite of all her difficulties.

Number Six arrived with the blast of a school van's horn. It was Mr. Ramaswamy, the driver who waited for Neha every morning as she raced to catch the school bus. Neha offered him an affectionate greeting along with all his Number brothers.

'Hello Neha!' said Number Six. 'Has Number Five been complaining about my winning every time we play cards?'

'In fact, I was about to remind Neha about the six faces of Karthikeya, Ganesha's brother,' said

Number Five. 'She will remember you every time she goes into a Lord Muruga or Shanmuga temple.

'Yes, I know Shanmuga means the Six-faced One!' said Neha excitedly.

'I am two triangles, making a star
Knowing me well, will take you far
A Perfect Number I'm pleased to be,
All my divisors equal up to me!'

Sang Number Six.

Neha's mind was racing by now. 'The divisors of six are 1, 2 and 3,' she said. '1+2+3=6!'

'Yes, and $1 \times 2 \times 3$ is also equal to 6', said Number Six.

'You're really Perfect!' said Neha admiringly.

'Thank you,' said Number Six with his hands folded in a *namaste*.

'We are ready to move on to brother Seven!' said Number Five.

'But it is quite far, how do we go there? Uchaishravas has flown back to the heavens,' said Number Three.

'Let me have the pleasure of sending you on my special peacock,' said Number Six. To Neha's utter delight, he turned aside and called 'Aa-aa-uh,

Aa-aa-uh!' in a perfect imitation of a peacock's call. A truly majestic peacock began gliding towards them and opened its beak in an answering call. Then it waited patiently for them to get on its back for their flight to meet Number Seven.

* * *

As Neha glided through the air with the others on the back of this beautiful bird, she was thinking, 'How many more adventures will I have with these beautiful numbers? How wonderful to have them as my friends!'

The perfect arch of a seven-coloured rainbow greeted them when they landed. Neha looked in wonder and awe upon the sight and remarked, 'Seven is indeed a special number. This rainbow has seven colours and there are seven notes in music. I must pay attention to Number Seven.'

When Neha first gazed upon Number Seven, she almost did not recognise him. He was tall and stooping, with a face that was slightly asymmetrical. One side of his jaw was longer than the other, so that his chin was placed off-centre, not pointing straight towards the ground. Number Seven scratched his chin and the gesture reminded Neha. 'Uncle Bhaskar!' she exclaimed aloud. Number Seven held out his arms to her, a pleased smile on his face.

'I am so happy to see you,' said Neha. 'You didn't come to visit us last Diwali.'

'No Neha,' said Number Seven. 'I couldn't get away from my work. The wonderful work with numbers.' Neha's Uncle Bhaskar was a mathematical scientist at a large scientific research establishment in Mumbai.

'I wish you *had* come,' said Neha. '*Amma* often scolds me and says I am not at all like her family. She wonders why I am so poor with numbers, when you and her other brothers and cousins are all scientists and mathematicians.'

'Well, Neha,' said Number Seven. 'I am very sorry to hear about your troubles with numbers and about Lakshmi scolding you. I must have a talk with my sister when I next visit your home. But don't you worry. You are now on your way to visit Zero. Once you have been there, everything will be easy!'

'Everyone tells me the same thing,' said Neha wonderingly.

'You're well on your way with Number Seven
I am prime, make a week, point to sages in
heaven.
Any power of 2 if you divide by me,
4, 2, or 1 will your remainder be.'

'There are seven days in a week and seven *Saptarishi* stars in the Great Dipper!' said Neha, understanding immediately. She had learnt to pay attention to all the number songs. 'Now test the other two lines. 2 raised to 3 is equal to 8. Divide that by 7 and I get 1 as the remainder. 2 raised to 6 is 64. Divide 64 by 7 and I get 1 as the remainder. I get it. I'll remember this Uncle Bhaskar.'

'You definitely will, Neha,' said Number Seven. 'But wait! Having come this far you must show me that you are well in tune with things in the world of numbers. I want you to find me a number among all these.'

He waved a hand and many different numerals began walking on the grass towards them, 147 and 28 and 64 and 124 read Neha, recognising the moving figures. More numbers arrived. When Number Seven had assembled enough of them, he called a halt with his hand.

'Now, Neha,' he said, 'find me my square among all these numbers.'

Neha ran her eyes along all the assembled numbers, then began walking purposefully towards 49. She went and stood next to it.

'Here's your square, Uncle Seven!' she said.

'Congratulations, Neha. You deserve to move ahead to meet my remaining brothers, Eight and Nine and of course, King Zero.'

His words of encouragement were sweet to Neha's ears, but she hardly had a moment to savour them. The angry witch had appeared again.

'Why do you insist on continuing this journey?' asked the witch. 'Do you think I have exhausted my powers? It is not so easy to defeat me, I promise you. Let me show you the might of *jala.*'

She once more invoked the elements with a *mantra* and some ashes flung into the air. Water began gushing towards them from all sides. Neha and her number friends were trapped in a flood!

As they were tossed from side to side upon the waves, Neha struggled to stay afloat. She remembered the words of Saraswati Devi, 'Do not be afraid, even if the way is difficult and dangerous.' In her mind, she prayed, 'O *Eeswara*, do something or I will drown!'

Shiva appeared in the sky with trident in hand. He shook his matted locks and they flew open.

Immediately, all the water around them, the acres and acres of high, blue waves, got absorbed into Shiva's hair! Neha had just an instant in which to look up at Him with great gratitude, before He vanished again.

All the Numbers were ecstatic. 'You have received the blessings of Shiva Himself!' they told Neha. 'He has saved us all from drowning in those fearsome flood waters.'

The fairy godmother was smiling. 'You have understood the power of prayer, Neha,' she said.

But they were to receive a greater proof of Shiva's blessings. As they turned to move forward, they found a very tall, powerful Nandi waiting for them. 'Shiva has left Nandi for us to travel further!' exclaimed Neha.

'Yes, it seems He has arranged things in His own way,' agreed the Numbers.

* * *

Before her Neha saw the domain of Number Eight. A familiar figure waited for her next to a large shady tree. Her heart missed a beat when she recognised the figure as Mr. Guhan, the Principal of her school.

en a remarkable thing happened. As Neha approached Number Eight in the company of the other numbers, seated comfortably atop the majestic Nandi she felt a surge of confidence very different from the apprehension she had felt in the Principal's room when Ms. Eswaran had complained about her. What was there to fear? She was doing very well, able to understand the secrets the Numbers told her and her brilliant uncle Bhaskar, or rather, Number Seven, had told her that she was on her way to meet king Zero. Neha held her head high and approached Number Eight.

'I am proud of you Neha,' said Number Eight in his deep and serious voice. 'I always knew you had great potential and you have come very far in the steps leading to Zero's court. You will soon have an audience with him and nothing will give me greater pleasure than to accompany you.'

'Thank you, Number Eight,' said Neha, looking up at him with shining eyes.

'I'm solid, I'm strong, I'm clearly square,
I have a reputation for being very fair.
A thousand can be made up of eight of me
I reverse the order of one, you will see.'

Neha looked astonished, even though she had learnt to keep pace with all the Number songs. 'How can eight eights make a thousand?' she asked. 'I thought it was 64.'

'I will show you,' said Number Eight. 'Add 888 to 88, then to 8, another 8 and one more 3.'

Neha was looking for a place to scribble the sum, but to her amazement, a row of skipping, dancing and jumping number '8s' came tumbling towards her from the tree under which they stood. Neha looked up at its

```
  888
   88
    8
    8
    8
 1000
```

branches in surprise. 'Is this a tree where 8s grow?' she asked.

'This is one of the special advantages of being in Zero's kingdom,' said Number Eight. 'We can make numbers perform whatever we desire. Now, do the addition.'

Neha caught one of the skipping number 8s, and found that it felt like a slightly rubbery toy in her hand. She placed it on the ground, then caught others to form the 888. When Neha had finished forming the sum it looked like this:

'How wonderful!' exclaimed Neha. 'I had no idea that 1000 was made up of 8s, like this.'

Number Eight had one more hint for Neha. 'Do you remember the multiples in the multiplication table of Number One, and how they go forward in an ascending order, 1, 2, 3, 4, 5, and so on?' he asked.

'Of course,' said Neha.

'Well, just look at the multiples in my multiplication table. If you add the digits and bring them down to the last single digit, you will find that the table moves in the same way as Number One, except that the digits are in a descending order,' said Number Eight.

'8, 16, that is $1+6=7$, then 24, that is $2+4=6$, 32, whose digits add up to 5... Yes! I can see it happening. Its 8, 7, 6, 5, 4, 3, 2, 1, 0, then again, the same pattern,' said Neha.

Number Eight gave Neha a pleased pat on her back. 'You have just Nine to meet now, before you are taken to meet Zero. Great going, Neha!' he said.

Now Neha was surrounded by all her encouraging Number friends. She was close to the gates of Zero's court and they were all recalling her difficulties in reaching there. 'There was one time I thought we will all be fried chicken!' said Number Three in a reminiscent vein. 'What about the floods?'

asked Number Five. 'I don't even know how to swim!'

'I really hope the evil witch will leave us alone now,' said Neha. But even as she spoke, the witch appeared, with a frightening expression on her face.

'You are truly a pest,' she said to Neha. 'And you Numbers, you should know better than to indulge her. Since you have insisted on bringing her this far, it is left to me to prevent her from going further! Don't forget I still have the power of *Vayu*!

So saying, she muttered another *mantra* and invoked the winds. A shrieking hurricane began around them and the cyclonic winds were so strong, that Neha and her Number companions were all picked up off the ground! They began whirling in space and as Neha was completely helpless against the wind, she felt her limbs pulled back and forth in the currents of the hurricane. Would she ever reach the ground? She looked pleadingly at her fairy godmother, who closed her eyes in prayer.

The serene face of Vishnu, emerging for a brief instant from the blue of the sky, told them that the fairy godmother's prayers had been heard. In the next instant, Garuda appeared, flying strongly through the winds and lifted each of them effortlessly in his strong claws. He collected them all and set them back down on safe ground, where they stood before the home of Number Nine, which resembled a temple.

The sound of devotional music, of *nadaswaram* and *thavil* reached Neha's ears and caused goosebumps to appear on her arms. In a moment of complete understanding, she knew she was about to meet Number Nine and she also knew Nine's beloved face.

Then Number Nine stepped out to greet her and Neha rushed forward to be hugged by Murthy Gurukal. She was crying a little, but they were only tears of joy.

'Brave, bright girl,' said Number Nine. 'I have been waiting to take you to see Zero. Come, there is some sweet *prasad* for you to refresh yourself.'

As Neha tasted the sweet, *ghee*-laden *pongal*, it suddenly reminded her of how long it was since she had eaten her last festive meal at the house of Number Two. She was hungry and the *prasad* was satisfying her in a way food rarely did.

She told Number Nine, 'I already know how special you are. There are nine planets in our solar system and *navagraha* deities in our temples. In music, dance and literature, we learn about the *navarasas,* and jewellery made with the *navaratnas* is considered most auspicious.'

'So you have noticed how often I crop up in your day to day life,' said Number Nine. 'You are an observant girl.'

'I perform more miracles than everyone else
I am the most intriguing, the folklore tells.
My multiples all, always add up to nine
I play piano on the digits of my table, just fine!'

He sang.

'I know that all the multiples of nine add up to nine if brought to the single digit,' said Neha. 'For instance, $9 \times 3 + 27$, $2 + 7 = 9$, or $9 \times 12 = 108$, and $1 + 0 + 8 = 9$.'

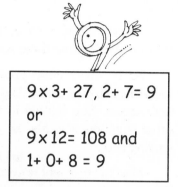

$9 \times 3 + 27$, $2 + 7 = 9$
or
$9 \times 12 = 108$ and
$1 + 0 + 8 = 9$

'What about my multiples in the first nine steps of my multiplication table?' asked Number Nine. 'They first begin 18, 27, 36, 45, then return 54, 63, 72, and 81! Isn't that like pressing two keys of the piano in a special tune?'

'Yes, it is,' said Neha. 'Show me some other intriguing things you do,' she begged.

'Well, take any number, like 87594,' said Number Nine. 'Scramble the digits in any order you like,' he said, and Neha answered, '49578'.

'OK, now subtract the smaller number 49578 from the original number 87594, and add up the

---

digits of the remainder, which is 38016,' said Number Nine.

Neha did a rapid mental addition and got 18 as the answer, which again reduced to nine in the single digit.

'Lovely, Number Nine,' she said. 'I can't wait to tell my friends about these special qualities of yours.'

As Number Nine patted Neha's head in a familiar gesture, it seemed as if her path to Zero was now secure. She basked in the appreciation of the other Numbers who had all gathered about her in a smiling circle.

Had the moment arrived when she would meet Zero?

9

In the Presence of Zero

The witch had reached Zero before Neha did. She tried to talk to him about Neha and set his mind against her.

'Please don't allow Neha to come near you. She is a wicked girl,' she pleaded with Zero.

'There is no need to tell me about her, I know her very well. I make my own judgement of people,' replied Zero.

'Well, then your judgement is wrong. It will be a great injustice to those who are brilliant in mathematics, if you show special favours to this stupid girl,' said the witch.

'I give no favours nor do I take favours. I have a busy day ahead of me. Please do not disturb me any more,' said Zero.

'Then you will not listen to me?' asked the witch.

'I will not be browbeaten by anybody,' said Zero. 'If I find the girl is no good, I will send her back. But I will be the judge of that, not you!'

The witch had to retreat, mumbling sulkily to herself. 'If Zero will not listen, I will have to take matters in my own hands,' she decided.

She sat in a secluded spot to conduct a special *puja* with a sacrificial fire into which she poured blood and ashes and coloured potions to produce dozens of small, vicious demons. These dark devils began prancing about near her and she commanded them, 'Go, go and stop Neha from meeting Zero!'

Neha and her Number friends approached the palace of Zero in a truly awesome procession. The prancing baby elephants had changed to tall, stately, majestic adults — nine of them, meant to carry the nine Numbers. Neha and the fairy godmother sat in a separate chariot and all of them moved forward in a grand, celebratory manner. Number One was playing the flute, Number Three was playing the triangle and Number Six and Number Eight were

116

chipping in with percussion beats on the drums. The elephants moved in time to this heavenly music, with their steps matching each other's. Neha was absolutely thrilled.

All of a sudden, small prancing devils that clutched at arms and throats, that sharply bit and stung, that seemed as if they would strangle the merry procession appeared as if from nowhere. These demons swarmed and surrounded Neha and her friends and their attacks terrified the group. The witch appeared as their leader, commanding them to be ever more vicious.

'What do we do against these *Rakshasas*?' asked Neha. 'It seems as if they will destroy us!'

'Neha, you have the power to call on Lord Ganesha. Pray to him now!' reminded the fairy godmother.

'Neha call Lord Ganesha to help us all!' shouted Neha's Number friends.

With all her mental might, Neha thought of Lord Ganesha. 'Please save me and my Number friends from these evil attackers!'

The sound of booming thunder made her open her eyes. She was completely stunned to see the huge form of Lord Ganesha, who swept away the demons with one stroke of his massive trunk, then glared at the cowering and fearful figure of the witch.

'You wicked woman! Instead of encouraging the girl and helping her become friends with numbers, you have been doing your best to stop her progress! You deserve to be punished and I shall punish you!'

The nine elephants began moving in a circle, surrounding the witch on the ground, as she sat huddled before the giant form of Ganesha.

'Forgive me!' pleaded the witch. 'I did not understand that she is really interested in numbers. Please do not punish me! I shall trouble her no more!' her cries were getting desperate.

'It is not enough that you do not trouble her again. You must promise never to do what you have done to her to another child. No student should have to suffer humiliation and agony in the study of numbers. Don't you understand the sacred duty of a teacher to encourage and uplift a student?' thundered Ganesha.

'I promise never to behave with another student as I have done with Neha. I promise! I am sorry!' sobbed the witch. She looked a truly miserable sight.

'Since you have shown repentance, you escape my punishment this time. But remember, I am always guarding those who are engaged in the study of numbers!' said Ganesha.

He then looked at Neha with kind and humourous eyes. 'It was good you remembered to call me, Neha,' he said. 'You have my blessings.' He raised a hand in blessing as He spoke. Then he said. 'Are you confident now, that I always have my eye on you?'

'Yes!' said Neha. She kneeled before Him and closed her eyes with her hands folded in prayer. But when she opened her eyes again, Ganesha was gone, only the procession of elephants was once more carrying her to Zero's palace.

It had all been leading up to this. Neha's magical sojourn in the world of numbers was meant to bring her finally to the presence of the acknowledged ruler of numbers — Zero himself. As she entered the huge hall in a crystal and moonstone palace, Neha was completely awed.

All the Numbers from One to Nine were alongside her. Behind her, they were singing a song:

'She's here, she's near
She's dried up her tears
She's happy, she's dear
She's said good-bye to fear'

Neha was more thrilled than ever that they were singing about her. The love and affection the Numbers had showered on her had touched her deeply. How could she ever have hated numbers or thought they hated her?

The inside of the palace was even more beautiful than the outside, which had radiated a brilliance in the light of the sun that Neha had never seen before. Within the large domed hall, a tall, diamond-encrusted throne was set and a row of smaller seats encircled the space, giving Zero's court the feeling of being a gathering of friends, deep in discussion.

In the carved and well-lit interior, Neha looked back once more at the Numbers escorting her and glimpsed something else — a shamed, shadowy figure furtively creeping into the grand hall. It was the witch who had attempted to trouble her all the way, when she was trying to reach Zero. Now the witch looked chastened and quietly followed in Neha's wake.

As for Zero? He stood up and stared sombrely at Neha, sending a thrill running down her spine. He was tall and broadly built, with long robes embroidered with all kinds of mathematical symbols. His flowing beard reached down his chest. His eyes were piercing, but not unkind and his expression was serious, till Neha reached quite close. Then his face broke into a warm, encouraging, welcoming smile.

'Welcome to my kingdom, Neha,' he said. 'I hope all the Numbers have been treating you well.'

'Y-y-ee-s,' stammered Neha. She felt completely awed and was not able to reply with her usual effervescence. Zero stepped forward, bent down and took her hand. Her small hand seemed to disappear into his large and gentle one.

Holding Neha by the hand, Zero faced the hall where a gathering of people was seated in a circle. He made a sweeping gesture with his arm and indicated all these people to Neha. 'Here you are, Neha. You see before you many of the individuals who have been especially dear to me. There is Archimedes, there Pythagoras, Einstein is sitting there and Ramanujan by his side. Sir Isaac Newton is here too, while Hypatia, the renowned daughter of Theon finds much to discuss with Bhaskaracharya and Aryabhatta. Perfect contentment reigns here — though there is also the playful squabbling of friends. You see the reason why everyone is so happy is because they are immersed in the enjoyment of something they love — the sheer joy of numbers.'

Neha looked at the august group of the world's best mathematicians with wide open eyes. They were all there, quite recognisable from the pictures in the charts in Ms. Eswaran's precious Maths Room. Pythagoras and Archimedes were bearded and Aryabhatta had a scholarly tuft at the back of his head. Bhaskaracharya was smiling at Neha! He beckoned to her and she went forward.

'Dear Neha, you remind me so much of my own daughter,' said Bhaskaracharya. 'My own Lilavati after whom I named my most aesthetic work on numbers. I hope you grow to work on the special aspects of mathematics too. One day, you should take your place amongst us.'

Hypatia, the great mathematician from Alexandria, who had been such a revered teacher to hundreds of students from 370 to 415 AD was seated just near Bhaskaracharya. She too called Neha to her side. 'Remember, apart from your love of mathematics, what you will need in your life as a woman is courage my girl. Plenty of courage,' she said. Neha nodded. She was fascinated by the way Hypatia's hair was swept up to the top of her head and kept in place by a hair clip of ebony and camel bone.

Another lady present, the American mathematician Louise Hays looked with a lot of interest at Neha. 'You are from India, aren't you? Do you like the world of numbers?'

This time Neha's voice came out without any hesitation. 'Yes, I love it,' she said. Inwardly she felt surer than ever.

While Neha was still being greeted by the mathematicians present, it seemed as if the discussion between them gathered momentum. Archimedes and Aryabhata began to discuss their relative definitions of 'pi'. Albert Einstein was being questioned about the 'Unified Field Theory' he had sought, whereby the phenomena of gravitation and electromagnetism could be derived from one set of equations. Everyone present was becoming involved in the question of whether it was enough for mathematics to be appreciated for itself, or whether the applications of it were more important.

'With due regard to the achievements of science and technology, I think it is still important to approach Maths only in a spirit of curiosity and discovery — not to ask every moment, "What is this for?" The constant asking of such a question interferes with true appreciation of Maths,' said Ramanujan. 'Hear, hear!' was the general cry that responded to this statement.

'I mean, do you go to the London Philharmonic for a concert, and ask what the symphony being played there is *for*?' asked Sir Isaac Newton.

'What is the debate about? All relations can be reduced to numbers. All things are numbers,' said Pythagoras. 'Astronomy, music, even natural phenomena, everything reinforces the mathematical nature of the universe!'

Invigorated by the discussion, Albert Einstein picked up a violin and began to play a cheerful tune. The great mathematicians got up and began to dance! To Neha's surprise, they began to surround her, so that she was soon inside a circle of dancing mathematicians!

Neha looked at Zero. He smiled and nodded to her, and said, 'Yes Neha, all these brilliant mathematicians are looking for someone like you to carry on their work in the world. We would all like to crown you the Princess of Numbers!'

Neha was speechless with happiness. Zero continued, 'But before we do that, we want to know how you have been spending your time in the Number world. If you answer my question, I will crown you myself.'

Neha grew a little tense. What would her test be? 'So Neha,' said Zero, 'have you thought about my qualities?'

'Yes, of course,' said Neha, a little breathlessly. 'Many people consider you a trouble maker, as you need special handling. But I know that you are the King of Numbers.'

She waited for Zero to burst into song. But he didn't. Instead, fixing Neha with his clear and direct gaze he intoned, in a deep and serious voice, those qualities that were to become forever unforgettable to Neha.

'I am the void that holds it all,' he said. 'I am that vast nothingness that cannot be measured, yet all numbers exist in me. I am both negative and positive and at the same time, neither negative nor positive. Any number plus me gives that same number. Any number minus me gives that same number too. Multiplying any number by me gives myself — Zero. Dividing by me is not allowed in the mathematical world. I am used to 'round off' other numbers in commercial transactions, but never used the way other numbers are used in daily life. Therefore, I am the purest of them all.'

Neha was absorbing everything he told her with an expression of complete concentration. She understood now why the other numbers had constantly referred to Zero as their king and why it was all his kingdom. He was greater than the greatest and at the same time smaller than the smallest!

'Now Neha, just answer my question. If you multiply 6587109 by me, what will your answer be?'

In a flash, Neha replied, 'Any number that is multiplied by you, becomes you! The answer is Zero!'

All the mathematicians and Numbers present clapped and rejoiced. Zero smiled and said, 'Congratulations, Neha! You deserve to be crowned princess of the Number World!'

He stepped forward to place the crown on her head and Neha felt her heart would burst with happiness. 'I love numbers!' she declared. As the crown slipped on her head, Neha felt the whole scene around her slip away and dissolve. She looked around, but everything was turning faint and fading away.

10

A Time to Rejoice

The elephant had refused to leave, even after the girl injured in the accident had been admitted to the hospital where it had brought her. While doctors inside did their best to stop the bleeding from Neha's head and another injury on her arm, Shakti stayed outside. She was there when Seenu arrived and Neha's frightened and distraught parents, who had been told of their daughter's accident by Prashant.

Murthy Gurukal was accompanying Neha when she was brought to the hospital by Shakti. His heart was wrung by the thought of Neha making her way home in the rain. How he wished he had accompanied her then! Mr Guhan, the school Principal arrived, accompanied by Ms Nandini and Ms Eswaran, Neha's Maths Teacher. The harsh teacher was suffering agonies of guilt at the way she had treated Neha. She joined the group keeping vigil at Neha's bedside.

Shakti watched them all go in and although she, being a pachyderm and not a human, was not allowed to enter the hospital itself, her vigil at the gates of the hospital was no less worried or patient. In vain did her keeper Muthuraman try to take her back to the temple quarters for her dinner and rest. The elephant just refused to budge till there was further news of Neha.

The night passed with agonising slowness. Neha's mother was weeping silent tears, watching the pale, bandaged face of her only child. Her mind was replaying all Neha's lovable actions — how she loved to draw *kolam*, how cheerful she always was, (except when she had been scolded) how she specially asked for the daily banana before leaving for school (her mother thought this was because Neha was conscious of eating a balanced diet!) and many other small incidents that she wished she would be fortunate enough to experience again. Neha's father was pacing the room, trying to speak to the doctors every now and then and looking out at the waiting elephant from the window. 'How thankful I am that this blessed elephant managed to rescue Neha!' he was thinking. 'It is truly a God-sent elephant.' Murthy Gurukal left late at night, after putting a reassuring hand on Neha's father's shoulder. 'She will be all right soon,' he said, 'She is one of Pillaiyar's youngest devotees. He will nurse her back to health soon.'

Although Neha did not regain consciousness that night, her parents were thankful that the tests performed on her had shown that she did not have any breakage of bones, or other major injuries. Only the gash on her head, which had needed eight stitches, and some other bruises, including a long wound on her arm, gave cause for anxiety. But the most worrying thing was Neha not returning to consciousness.

Seenu the milkman had come to the hospital and stayed to offer what help he could to Neha's parents. When dawn was approaching, he tiptoed into the room where Neha lay, wanting to inform her father that it was time for him to leave for his milk rounds. But instead he had a pleasant surprise awaiting him.

Before Neha's father could worry further, Neha opened her eyes. The remarkable thing was her eyes looked bright and happy, instead of the dazed and unfocused eyes of someone returning to consciousness after a gap of several hours.

'*Amma!*' said Neha with utmost pleasure. '*Appa!* Oh! How happy I am to be back!'

'Oh Neha!' sobbed her mother. 'We are so happy too! You gave us all a great fright.'

Her father gripped Neha in a tight hug and said gruffly, 'Thank God you're alright princess!'

Neha saw her Principal and teachers. 'We have been so worried about you. We could not bear the news of your accident!' said the Principal.

'I am sorry to have caused you such pain, Neha,' said Ms Eswaran. 'I will try to teach you in a better way...I didn't know.'

Neha surprised everyone present by interrupting her with her next words.

'Don't worry, Miss,' she said. 'I will do better too. I love numbers.'

Her father turned to look at her with surprised eyes. 'That's wonderful,' he said. 'Now just let me tell that elephant you are all right. Or better still, I'll wheel your cot a little closer to the window and you can give her a wave. Shakti's been standing there ever since she brought you here last night!'

In a few moments, Neha sat up in bed and waved to Shakti's large shape, visible near the hospital gate silhouetted against the morning light. She felt utterly, completely happy.

Glossary

Aadi taala	The name of an eight-beat rhythm in Carnatic classical music.
Akshara	Each beat of a *taala*.
Amma	Mummy.
Appa	Father.
Appam	Deep fat fried sweets made of rice powder and *gur*.
Been	The snake charmer's flute.
Brahma	The Creator in the Holy Trinity.
Channa	Chick peas / gram.
Dahi-vadai	Fritters of batter made from ground pulses, which are then soaked in curds.
Dhoti	A kind of clothing, often worn by males all over India to cover the lower part of the body. It consists of a long cloth knotted round the waist, passed between the legs and tucked in at the back.
Eeswara	God.

Garuda	The king of the birds, an eagle who is the mount of Lord Vishnu.
Ghagra-choli	Traditional Indian ankle-length skirt and mini-blouse.
Ghee	Clarified butter.
Goddess Saraswati	The Hindu Goddess of learning — in particular the arts and literature.
Halwa	A sweet preparation of semolina/flour/vegetables which is first fried in *ghee* (clarified butter), then boiled. Sugar, dry fruits and other condiments are then added to taste.
Indra	The king of the Hindu Gods.
Jala	Water.
Kalidasa	The greatest Sanskrit poet, one of the 'Navratnas' of Vikramaditya's court.
Kartikeya	The six-faced son of Shiva, who rides a peacock.
Kolam (or rangoli)	Simple or intricate patterns drawn with white or coloured powder, usually in front of the doorstep. Drawing it regularly is supposed to augur well for the household.
Krishna	The cowherd God of the Hindu pantheon.

Kurta	Loose pullover shirt traditionally worn by Indians.
Lord Ganesha	The elephant-headed God of wisdom, worshipped by the Hindus as He is supposed to remove all obstacles and guarantee success.
Mama	Maternal uncle.
Mami	Auntie / wife of maternal uncle.
Mathra	Subdivision of a beat.
Mridangam	Percussion instrument used to mark the rhythm of Bharat Natyam.
Nadaswaram	Musical wind instrument rather like the clarinet, popular in South India.
Navagraha	Nine planets.
Navaratnas	Nine gems.
Navarasa	The gamut of nine human emotions through which literature — particularly drama — music and dance are supposed to run.
Pakoras	Fritters / batter fries.
Papad or appalam	Ultra-thin ready-to-fry roundels made of rolled out dough of gram / pulses / wheat flour.
Pillaiyar	Lord Ganesha.
Puja	Prayer / worship.

134

Pongal	The sweet preparation made of rice, jaggery, milk etc. for special religious occasions in Tamil Nadu.
Poories	Small round fried pieces of unleavened bread.
Prasad	Offerings made to the deities, which are then distributed among the faithful.
Radha	Krishna's special love (often considered the symbol of human yearning for Divine Union).
Shiva	The ascetic God, Destroyer, who along with Brahma, Creator, and Vishnu, Protector, forms part of the Holy Trinity of the Hindu pantheon.
Taala	(Prounced as Taal in Hindi) Beat or rhythm of a song or dance.
Thavil	Oval-shaped shallow utensil, which is also used as a percussion instrument.
Uchaishravas	The winged horse of Indra.
Vayu	The Wind.
Veena	Stringed instrument of the lute family.
Vishnu	The Protector in the Holy Trinity.